HOBART

another literary journal

issue no. six

HOBART #6
Summer '06

Subscriptions: $17 for 1 year (2 issues); $32 for 2 years (4 issues)
Inquire for institutional rates

Submissions are accepted year-round

For more info regarding submissions, subscriptions, general questions, or anything else, please visit the website or send us a letter:

www.hobartpulp.com

HOBART
PO Box 1658
Ann Arbor, MI 48103

ISSN 1544-788X
ISBN-10: 0-9749541-2-8
ISBN-13: 978-0-9749541-2-7

Cover painting by Perry Vasquez

This painting was originally used for the cover art for
Maquiladora's *A House All On Fire.*
http://www.maquiladora.cx/

Hobart is edited by: Aaron Burch
It is made better by: Elizabeth Ellen, Brooks Callison, and Mike McGowan
The website is: Savannah Schroll, Claudia Smith, and Jensen Whelan, with Sean Carman as photo editor

Thanks.

CONTENTS
(in order of appearance)

And every once in a while
I need some heavy metal tunes.
How 'bout you?

"Second-Hand Slayer Records"
Roy

featured artist

Home on the Range

perry vasquez

Home, home on the range
Where the deer and the antelope play
Where seldom is heard, a discouraging word
And the skies are not cloudy all day
— *Traditional*

If he's got golf clubs in his truck or a camper in his driveway, I don't hire him.
— *Lou Holtz (American Football coach, 1937-1980)*

1

IN THE SUMMER OF 1972, my father bought a 1970 GMC camper with a 12-foot shell on the back. The cab was white with custom chrome, and the camper shell had weirdly textured sheet metal siding that reminded me of a wicker basket. Reflectors studded the corners, and various filters, grills, ports, louvered windows, and sliding windows punctured the surface. I especially loved all the goofy utility hookups like the electrical sockets, drainage outlets, and stuff like that sticking out on the sides. My father customized the chassis by adding a larger rear bumper and attaching a mount for an extra gas can next to the rear door. Later we would need that gas can. And it was that exact bumper that would come to mind 8 years later in 1980 when I first saw the cover art for the Talking Heads album *Fear of Music*. It was very cool, like a floral wallpaper motif set in sheet metal is cool.

2

In 1972. my father was a 42-year-old son of an immigrant farm worker and a member of the rising middle class in Escondido, California. He was a high school coach with an accounting business on the side and he was smart and ambitious enough to be told by others he should consider running for public office. He gave it some thought but decided hell no because, "If you go into politics you lose the right to go into a public bar and have a drink." I was 13 when he told me that and I already knew what he meant. So he stayed out of politics and instead became known as an unofficial mayor of the town, a result of his common sense, positive attitude, integrity, and willingness to be the "Mother Murphy".

3

My father stylized himself to the mainstream culture as the Energizer Mexican — always hustling his ass off and pumping up his friends, family, and assorted team members with motivational talk. He played baseball on his championship high school team in 1947. He has always drawn from an endless supply of the stuff that legendary short stops are made of. He was an excellent fielder, hitter, and an expert chatterbox, too. Anyone who ever played baseball knows the importance of chatter to the game. You always need at least one fuckin dude on your team with a fuckin motor mouth and a fuckin knack for antagonizing the fuck out of the other team if you want to win the psych-out part of the game. And my dad was that fuckin dude.

4

Camper shells always looked to me like big ass sheet metal pompadours sitting on the tops of trucks. Which I think is cool. Unfortunately, once inside, they lose a lot of their design bravado. In terms of design and styling the interiors are pure vanilla — they simulate the same visual effects found in most shiny new suburban ranch homes and kitchens. In my opinion, camper shells look like hairpieces. It's very odd.

Camper design advanced a lot after WWII thanks to the influence of aircraft design. You can see it in the formed metal siding with aerodynamic enhancements, curving edges and air slip surfaces. In the 20s and 30s it was possible to see people driving around the countryside with homemade campers that looked like the blending of an outhouse and a miniature cottage. That vernacular kind of American culture has always been very interesting to me.

5

The longest trip we ever made was to drive across the country to visit relatives in North Carolina. We started out in the beginning of August, a fucked up time of year to drive through the desert. There was not much way to escape the heat so we stopped every couple hours for Cokes and popsicles. Traveling through Arizona and New Mexico meant lots of souvenir stands, curio shops, and Stuckey's restaurants with their "native craft" gift shops and etc. The merchandise consisted mostly of sadly exploitative replicas of Indian artifacts. There were Indian beads, toy bows and arrows, fake hatchets, rubber knives, headdresses and moccasins overflowing from the aisles. My brother and I drooled over every bit of it. We couldn't wait to get it all back home and start a fight with it.

6

That summer of '72 we crossed many state borders. Cheerful welcoming signs awaited us, announcing we were about to cross into the greatest of the great 50 States. Their designs usually had pictures of flowers, birds, or fish printed on them, with maybe a drawing of the state's borders. This simple boosterism impressed me deeply. I expected happy natives to suddenly emerge from the scenery bringing a cornucopia of cool shit. It never happened but borders seemed like such friendlier places in those days... California, *Find Yourself Here.* Colorado, *Fresh Air and Fond Memories Served Daily.* Illinois, *Mile After Magnificent Mile*; *Right Here. Right Now.* The District of Columbia, *The American Experience*; *Taxation without Representation.* And then there's New Hampshire, *Live Free or Die.*

7

My favorite part of our GMC camper was the sleeping area above the cab. The view from there was very tight; there was just enough headroom to get up on my knees, maybe. Below the sleeper was a sliding window that connected the cab with the camper, like a hatch between a mothership and its pod. I knew about this because after the first mission to the moon in 1970, every kid my age knew what the LEM (lunar excursion module) was.

8

Night driving was the best. I can hardly think of a more hypnotic and sleep-inducing experience than lying up in that sleeper area, feeling the road below and watching the dark asphalt light up under the headlights. The dotted lines in the road zoomed at me like pulses of cool energy. On those night rides through the empty desert, my senses and imagination cranked out an endless flow of pictures and emotions like a gas powered internal combustion engine cranks out horse-power.

9

When I first heard of the idea Manifest Destiny, I thought, "That's sounds fuckin cool." I liked the spiritual scope of it. It was bold. It was Daniel Boone, Walt Disney, Roy Rogers, and Home on the Range. It wasn't apologizing for itself or sounding wimpy. It wasn't until years later, in high school, that I learned what Manifest Destiny actually meant. Then it dawned on me that people were capable of doing nasty fuckin things to each other in the name of progress.

John Gast painted a picture of Manifest Destiny in 1872. In it he portrays the nation's westward movement as a woman floating above the plains. Below her, Indians haul ass in retreat while settlers in covered wagons advance, resolutely, curiously, ready to fuckin ride over all dumbshits. She floats over it all gazing into the future, ignorant of the slaughter below. While leading her flocks to the Promised Land she graciously... hangs telegraph wire?

10

I can still hear the telephone poles and fence posts rushing past the 1970 GMC camper window somewhere at night with a whoosh whoosh whoosh sound, like angry hatchets being thrown through the air. It was always the last sound I heard before falling asleep.

Country Girl (Monster Truck Series), 1999
Perry Vasquez
Recycled Havoline 10w-30
on Arches print paper
22" x 30"

Lane 12

shellie zacharia

DARE TO DREAM, tattooed bowling queen, with your lemon-yellow fleecy flounced t-shirt, sleeves cut to show your muscled arms, your lime-green satin pants tight like whiskey down a throat, your red ringlet curls pulled high in a ponytail fountain. Take off your sunglasses, pop another piece of gum, it's time, sweet Juney Teresa Hart, to take the kingpin, take the hooks and wicked wrist twists, it's time to bring it on home for the Marion Four.

Catcalls and hootie hollers and finger snaps and leg slaps, as Juney Teresa Hart, the tattooed bowling queen of Majestic Lanes, makes her way to lane 12 for some cosmic karaoke bowling. Tuesday nights—cheap beer and cheese fries for two bucks. Rudy the Rude Dog manager plugging in equipment, tap tapping on the microphone, slapping shoes on the counter, line 'em up, sixes and nines and no more elevens, nope, got to wear twelves, but not for JTH, Miss Juney Teresa Hart, she's got her own shoes, custom designed—sweet toeless sling backs with red glitter stripes.

She's got her shoe size, 7, tattooed on the backs of her ankles, she's got Bowl or Die tattooed just above her left breast, she's got her gold flecked ball, initials carved in black, in a green velvet bag. She's ready.

Ooowee, Bowling Queen, she hears and she smiles, she tilts her head, she licks her lower lip and laughs, a laugh like wind chimes dipped in peanut butter pie. She gives a thumbs up with her bowling thumb, rubbed and primed with sweet almond cream. She puckers her pink painted lips and blows kisses to her teammates at the bar, Wilbur and Crazy Paula and Captain Hook, she struts on by Rudy the Rude Dog who stops slapping shoes, and she pauses at lane 12, breathes in, her lemon-yellow fleecy flounced t-shirt tight across her tattooed chest, and exhales a lingering puff of peppermint.

Crazy Paula joins her, hands Juney a beer, and says, "How you feeling Juney Teresa Hart?" And just for a moment, a moment so brief nobody would notice it—not even Shy Wilbur, who loves Juney Teresa Hart, who here at the bowling alley can't get past his blushing hellos though at home he has brilliant conversations with her picture, a photo clipped from the newspaper and hung on his refrigerator; he talks to sweet Juney while he makes his eggs in the morning, while he drinks his Bushmills at night—not even Shy Wilbur, would know that Juney Teresa Hart is full of heartbreak.

Juney pauses, her smile dips for an imperceptible moment. She says, "I'm doing okay, Paula, I'm doing okay." She lets her chewing gum snap, and then Juney Teresa Hart puts her green velvet bag down, takes a swig of beer and says, "Let's bowl."

Only Crazy Paula knows that Juney Teresa Hart is filled to the brim with sorrow, that the man she called her Demon Lover, the man she called Wish Come True, had taken her tattooed heart and torn it asunder just last month when he said, "Juney Teresa Hart, I think I've got to go back to Analee." "Going back?" Juney Teresa Hart had said, "Going back? But why?" She just couldn't believe it, the world had surely gone crazy, the cosmos had surely gone from Technicolor to gray, just how, why, oh why, why, why was Mister Decker Pancake going back to Analee? How ridiculous, Analee Pancake, who couldn't even bowl a 120, not even on Bumpers Up Night, not even with the full moon shining like a pearly bowling ball in the sky. Going back to Analee?

But Juney Teresa Hart is trying to get over it, she's cried her tears, she's tossed shoes at walls like she's throwing strikes, she's cursed the name of Decker Pancake, she's dreamed of his bowling ball cracking and splintering like splits, and so tonight, with the lights dimming and the disco ball spinning diamond flecks, and the sound of pins crashing, the sound of balls thumping on slicked floorboards, she says, "I'm doing okay."

Juney Teresa Hart is trying hard to be classy, so she doesn't send an evil eye toward lane 9, and she doesn't spit when Rudy calls out over the intercom that Decker has a call at the front desk, she just sits down at lane 12 and types in her name for the scoreboard, June Bug, and she punches the letters with surefingered swiftness.

Shy Wilbur slides into the seat next to Juney, he gives her a quick smile, he says, "Looking good, Juney," and he says it like a crackled whisper. "Why thank you, Wilbur," she says and she smiles, he smiles, she notices how white his teeth are, quite nice actually, much nicer than Decker's coffee stained yellows.

"Cosmic!" The word comes like a psychotic dream voice, it blares along lanes and reverberates in the gutters and it repeats, "Awwwwww, yeah, cosmic," and the words coming through the intercom signify the start of cosmic karaoke night, stroke of eleven, the neon tubing starts to blink and shiver then full force pink and green and orange lines of color brighten the walls and pin holders.

Cheers go upward, yahoos and yeehaws and yippeedees, and fists pump air and hands slap knees and backsides.

Beers are slugged and shoes are laced and stomped, except Juney Teresa Hart whose shoes don't tie, and Juney pulls her gold ball from her bag and puts it next to Shy Wilbur's blue grey duotone, and once again, "Cosmic! Oh yeah, it's cosmic," bounces through the intercom system and a siren wail, a bullhorn call, and Juney the tattooed bowling queen checks that the straps of her slingbacks aren't covering her number sevens, and then she looks to the front desk where Rudy, with his pompadour wig and his Buddy Holly glasses, is grinning wide, the microphone to his mouth, and a quick glance toward lane 9, and damn it all to hell, Juney's eyes meet Decker's, he's staring right at her, his mouth moves and she turns, spins in her glittery shoes before she can see what he's saying.

Damn it all to hell, Decker Pancake, with your shiny black hair and your wicked-ass grin and your hands that can palm a bowling ball and the curve of a woman's hip with the same ease. And damn you too, Analee Pancake, with your simpering whine about wifehood, and your begging and your knowledge that a man like Decker Pancake likes to be begged.

"You're up," Captain Hook calls out, and Juney grabs her ball, fits her soft fingers into the holes, pauses, steps, steps, lets the ball go, she sees pins explode, she sees the lights flash, she sees the neon bulbs brighten, she hears "Cosmic, get your cosmic on" and she turns, a strike, and there's Decker on his lane, his tongue stuck out in concentration, she slinks on back and shimmies into a seat before she has to watch, Decker, Decker, everywhere.

A voice like a turkey shot and dying now rises above the din of pins falling and balls tumbling, and Turbo Terry is at the karaoke machine singing "Rock Lobster" and things seem just a bit too tweaked, a bit too much for the bowling queen, she's got to sit down, have a drink, she feels her sorrow like one pin standing, she feels herself tensing, tightening, she feels like maybe, just maybe, she's not going to make it through the night.

"You okay?" she hears, and she opens her eyes and Shy Wilbur is crouched before her, and she says, "I'm okay," because that's what JTH is all about, being okay, even if Decker Pancake is just three lanes away and looking at her again.

"You're up," Crazy Paula calls out, and this is how it seems to go, with bowlers up and down and frame two, three, four, five, Juney noticing that a blister might be forming on one foot, and not ever has this happened with her customized bowling shoes, but tonight, yes, a little rubbing, a little irritation, and Freddy at the karaoke machine singing "Heartbreak Hotel," during frame six, and folks booing Freddy because Freddy has a voice like an old monkey crying, and there's Juney Teresa Hart with a not so impressive 106 in the seventh frame.

"Cosmic, dynamite, out of sight, it's cosmic night," Rudy with the microphone, his grin grown wider, and eight, nine, ten, tenth frame wind-up, with Juney Teresa Hart softly tracing the outline of her Bowl or Die tattoo, refusing to turn at the sound of Decker's calls, "June Bug, June Bug, please, please, please."

"You're up," Paula says, and Juney stands, she limps just a bit with the blister maybe getting bigger, and she takes her ball, bought on her thirty-fifth birthday, and she stands before lane 12, and she's about to take her first step when she hears the karaoke machine start up again and she hears, "This one's for you, June Bug," and there's Decker singing "You're just too good to be true," and his voice is of course not like a turkey or a monkey at all, but more like fire and she doesn't know why it happens or how it happens but that ball slips out of her hand and downward and those toe-less slingbacks don't do much for a girl sometimes, and she howls and curses and falls like a fluttering leaf, like a silk slip dropping. She sits down on the lane, and Decker Pancake with his redemption song stops midline while he stares at Juney Teresa Hart.

"It's cos..." Rudy begins, but he too sees Juney the tattooed bowling queen sitting down on lane 12, and he stops, he says into the microphone, "Juney?" and she grits her teeth and stares at her toes and shakes her head and listens to the silence around her. Freeze frame, with bowlers paused eating cheese fries and pizza slices, and bowlers powdering fingers and bowlers talking stocks and bonds and bowlers clapping for a nailed spare and bowlers mid-dance to the line, and everyone pauses to look to lane 12.

"You okay?" she hears in her ear, and crouched before her again is Shy Wilbur, and he's got his arm on her shoulder and his eyes are specked with the same gold as her bowling ball. "You okay?" he asks, and Juney says, "I don't think so," and she lets Wilbur help her up, she smiles as he lifts her in his shy arms and carries her away from lane 12 while the neon lights flash and the disco ball spins and Juney Teresa Hart lets Shy Wilbur dare to dream.

FIREWORKS

j. chris rock

YOUR EARS ARE RINGING, everybody's are. Under the hum and sudden silence you can hear Kit's amp crackling.

"What?" you ask.

"Donald thinks we're being shot at," says the Donald from London, the tall one with the blonde afro tipped back on his head like Garfunkel.

"Donald is correct," says the other Donald, the one from Manchester. He looks like what you think one of the nicer football hooligans would look like. The Donalds are exchange students who are, in fact, both named Donald and enjoy referring to themselves in the third person. They do this as often as possible.

These are your friends.

The Donalds are slumped on the couch. John, who is not a Donald, is behind the drum set. He is short, from D.C., and fully dedicated to wake and bake. John wears wrist-bands when he plays because that's what Mickey Hart does. Kit is on guitar, the only real musician in the band. You met

Kit in the dorms last semester. Adam is next to Kit, but he's more of a lead singer than a friend. The Donalds don't play anything. You're on bass.

"Fucking chins," says John.

You turn, bass and all, in time to see two fireballs shoot past the back window, one red, one orange. You hear two muted pops.

None of you belong in this neighborhood. The houses are new and far from campus. Only rich kids live out here. Every other house is packed with frat guys—chins, you call them—and sorority girls coasting extravagantly through summer break. The only way you can afford it is by packing six people into the two-bedroom house. Manchester Donald sleeps in one of the closets. Adam has a bed in the unfinished basement. He and his mousy girlfriend stay down there, doing whatever it is lead singers and mousy girlfriends do. You all work summer jobs and just make rent every month. The Donalds work at McDonald's and love saying so. You work at the mall record store, the not cool one.

The chins hate you, all of you. You know this because they let the air out of your tires, put dog shit in your mailbox and, now, the fireworks. The Fourth of July is next week. Giant fireworks tents have sprung up like black powder mushrooms on every road out of town. Ammo is in great supply.

You watch as another fireball, a yellow one, sails across the back deck. John is the first to act, always. He runs out onto the deck and starts taking wild swings with his drumsticks. Kit starts playing bad 80s guitar riffs. Adam mopes off downstairs while the rest of you watch John swing and miss, swing and miss, swing and miss and fall down. When he finally connects with one, blasting it into technicolor sparks, you all cheer. Kit plays charge.

This is what you do with your friends.

You stand at the edge of the hill behind your house, where the yard drops off into a forty-five degree slope of young trees and tangled plant life. You jump.

The hill being a hill, you go farther than you would on flat ground. If you jump four feet out, the ground below you drops away another six or seven feet. Which means you are now jumping twelve feet, fifteen, twenty. An arc, ever extending. The farther out you jump, the more the ground recedes, the farther you go.

You wait, watching John jump, then Kit, then the Donalds. Each flight ends in a distant crack and rustle. Then it's you, and you soar. You are a satellite, always falling, never landing. The acid stretches everything out. One long sailing moment of sky. Then comes the reality of the wind ripping by, your gut dropping. Then, boom. But less than a boom. The angle of the hill, the same sweet tilt that lets you fly, makes landing a gradual process. Empty air becomes twigs then red Missouri dirt then, at some point, you simply aren't moving anymore.

To do this on hallucinogens makes perfect sense. Take the war to the enemy. Do the most dangerous thing imaginable in order to stay safe. Jump.

It's hard for you to believe, but people actually show up. A lot of people. Your band, The Octogenarian Solution, has only played a few gigs around town and one in St. Louis, in what turned out to be a falafel restaurant with a cranky owner who lived upstairs and made you stop playing early. So you and John and Kit and, OK, Adam decide, fuck it. You'll make your own gig. Put up flyers downtown, plaster the partially deserted campus. You decide, let's play the driveway.

"Donald thinks you should do it on the Fourth of July." London Donald, Garfunkel Donald, had said it. But they had both been nodding.

So it's the Fourth and the cul-de-sac is packed. It's mostly a chin crowd, which you expected and came to terms with because they are an audience, any audience. They're clustered around the keg you stuck in the front yard.

Manchester Donald is wandering through the crowd in his bathrobe, bombed and eating cereal from a big yellow bowl. Kit is tuning and John is smoking up. Adam is downstairs. If history is any indication, the mousy girlfriend is caking eye liner on him.

Adam finally comes upstairs with black circles for eyes and ruby red lips. You all walk onto the driveway, into the glare of three table lamps with the shades off. John clicks off a beat with his sticks and you begin to play.

Your music doesn't belong here, any more than you. You listen to My Bloody Valentine, Slowdive, Pale Saints, Moose before they went country. You also listen to the Grateful Dead, but only for the drugs. You are primarily shoegazers, and the chin crowd is not going for it, not at all. More than one is giving you the finger.

You don't care. You are high and drunk. You feel the energy pouring out of the amps behind you. All the speed you took makes your body want to explode into action, but you keep it all potential, you move only your fingers, you shiver with electricity. Kit is roaring, more than noise, every possible melody layered into the static and chorus.

After eleven minutes, you end the first song. As Kit cuts off the feedback you hear someone in the crowd yell a frustrated "*Jee*-sus!" There is no applause. But there is something vastly satisfying in making the chins listen to you in order to drink free beer. Manchester Donald is standing in front of the crowd that's going out like a tide. He's eating cereal and smiling.

You start your second song. You get through only seven or eight minutes of it before the cops show up. Big men in dark blue wade through the receding crowd, hands on belts. You stop playing. Adam yells, "Blow me cops!" into the mic and takes off into the house. London Donald is together enough to realize the police should not be going into the house. He talks smoothly, promising the speedy retrieval of the lead singer. The job falls to you and John.

Adam has locked himself in the basement. You get him

to open the door a crack. You can hear the mousy girlfriend in there, giggling.

"You have to talk to the cops," you say.

"Yeah, well, I'd like to."

The fact that he says this but then does not move, just stares at you through the crack, is baffling. John begins to yell.

Adam eventually comes upstairs and outside, where he gets a thirty dollar ticket for disturbing the peace. He immediately begins to hound you and Kit and John to help pay the ticket. Your collective position is, you weren't the ones who told the cops to blow you, you don't owe.

You have to get out.

You have to leave because in the emergency room everyone's face is swimming. Everyone looks bruised and most of them, all of them, are coughing and yelling. It's all ramping up to a bad trip and that is not something you can deal with right now.

The Donalds handle their acid better than you do. They say they'll stay.

"Donald will wait for Kit."

So you and John leave. You walk under the calming orange glow of streetlights. You get some distance and you let yourself wonder what it's like to break your leg on acid. Is the pain worse? Kit had yelled like it was when he hit. You swear you heard the leg break, all the way from the top of the hill. Snap. Like the branches when you land, only bigger and wetter, like a carrot.

This was the first time you'd tried it at night, jumped. It was even better in the dark. Jump, and you're in a void. Jump, and you're riding the emptiness. That's what John told you when he got back to the top of the hill, all smiles and out of breath. There were leaves in his hair.

You jumped next, and John was right. Once your feet left the ground it all went away. Problem was, you couldn't tell when it was coming back. No soft landings at night. One minute you were sailing through nothingness. The next, the ground grabbed hold of your right leg and slammed you face-down into the dirt and twigs. Like being attacked by a pro wrestler. Ivan the Brambly, undefeated.

Back at the top you gave your own breathless thumbs up, but what you were really thinking was that you were done. One was enough. Then Kit jumped.

If you close your eyes, you can still see Kit's face. When you got to him at the bottom of the hill, he was all clenched teeth, sweating, screaming inside.

You try not to close your eyes. You blink as quickly as possible.

You and John walk to a grocery store. The shelves are filled with bright colors, clean and perfect things. You buy an oversized Crunch bar and decide you're not going to eat it. You just want to carry it around for a while.

There are four of you on the roof.

Kit is downstairs on the couch, leg in a cast, head in painkillers and shrooms. Adam is probably at the mousy girlfriend's place. He hasn't been around since the ticket incident last week. Which leaves four — John, the Donalds, and you — to fight the war.

You huddle below the roofline on the back side of the roof, the safe side. The twelve-inch tall Lenny Kravitz card-board statue you took from the record store is on top of the chimney. You call him Generalissimo Lenny. You salute him often. Generalissimo Lenny is surveying the battle.

An oversized bottle rocket, the expensive kind, skips off the front side of the roof. It trails sparks and smoke over you into the black night and, fabulously, explodes. The four of you dropped two tabs each, hours ago, and you are starting to peak. Necks tight, world shimmering. The explosion over-head is white plasma, energy dripping from the sky.

"The Donald thinks that was close." With tracers in your eyes you can't see his face, but the low London accent tells you it's Garfunkel Donald. This week, one of the Donalds found out Donald Trump goes by The Donald, so their shared name is now prefaced with a The. It doesn't make things any easier.

The chins are across the street this time, partying with their fellow chins. They are launching pricey rockets at you because, at sunset, they saw you and John and the Donalds standing in your front yard, spraying a hose into the air. The acid had just started kicking in and the water had been electric against the orange sky. You're pretty sure this is what set the chins off. Four nerd freaks worshipping a garden hose.

You were begging for it.

The volleys had started just after ten, smacking into the kitchen window. John ran into his room and returned with a grocery bag full of bottle rockets, eyebrows twiddling. This is when you realized he had been expecting this. John strutted out the back door, you and the Donalds followed. The plan was simple and, like the hill, made perfect sense. Counterattack from the roof. Of course.

Now you four are on the roof. You are tripping your collective nuts off and playing with recreational explosives. You are flying the Lenny flag.

You light dozeners of cheap bottle rockets and toss them like grenades. When you do it right—twisting the fuses in the middle, lighting them in one go—they all ignite at the same time and the combined energy propels them farther than any single bottle rocket. The dozener then rains a satisfying spread of explosions onto your intended target. This is your poor man's cluster bomb, one that occasionally works.

Your war goes in spurts. The four of you light and toss dozeners, then lie on your backs, safe below the roofline, and watch the chin counterattack detonate beautifully overhead. You crook your legs and set your feet against the gritty shingles. The tracers are indescribable, the language of gun powder and psychedelics. Occasionally, you prod the chins into another encore.

It is an unlucky shot that hits Generalissimo Lenny. Catches him in the hip and sends him spinning from his post. You see this happen. In your mind you hear the impact coming like a wave of static, then smack, a kaleidoscope off the pelvis. You see him spin once then tumble onto the shingles. Generalissimo Lenny slides down the roof, explosions overhead playing red and white off his glossy coating. His boa never flutters, his pose never shifts. At the bottom he tumbles a few times then, in slow motion, cartwheels over the side and disappears.

You think, holy shit. Generalissimo. You could all be doing that. Dropping, one by one, like bags of dim-witted cement to the hard ground below. Splitting open on impact. Pow. Pow pow pow.

"Blow me cops."

Adam had said that. Then he ran into your house where, not ten feet from the open door, the kitchen counter was littered with pot and shrooms, like a houseplant exploded. John's bedroom was just a few more steps. Next to his mattress on the floor, right there, a weathered sandwich bag filled with Jerry Claus acid, little teddy bears in Santa hats on each hit. Consequences upon consequences. Fines, jail, expulsion, parents. For the Donalds, deportation. From three amplified words, all of this.

Kit broke his leg on the hill. Could've been his neck. Could've been you.

You launched yourself off the hill like an invincible six-year-old, but one wrong landing, a few inches to the right, a few to the left, and you'd be paralyzed right now, food coming in through a tube, going out through another. Nothing would move but your eyes. Your arms and legs would shrink to sticks.

You think of even minor but horrible things. The band. Adam hasn't come back. Kit hasn't played since he broke his leg. The unspoken truth is that the band is no longer. You aren't a band anymore, you're just fucked up near instruments.

This is bad. Worse than the emergency room. Steeper, definitely. Even with your eyes closed, you can feel the tilt. The roof doesn't want you. The ground does.

Breathing isn't happening on its own. You have to think about it. Expand your chest, suck in the air, hold it for a second, let it back out. Do it again. Breathe. Again. Stop and you'll die. You are panicking. You know this, which makes you panic more. You are caught in the freakout loop. You're vaguely aware that your teeth feel soft.

Then you hear it. Over the freaked breaths and the grind of your slowly imploding jaw, you hear an absence of rockets. And you hear music, notes that sing in your head.

Oh say can you see.

You open your eyes. The Donalds are looking over the roofline. John is standing up, watching whatever it is. You roll over, keeping as flat as possible, hanging the fuck on. You pull yourself up and look.

Kit is out front. He has wheeled his amp into the driveway and, leg off to one side like a giant white kickstand, he is wailing on his guitar, belting out a Hendrix-style Star Spangled Banner with screeching asides and notes bent all to hell. He is beyond Hendrix. Kit swerves his anthem into the ditch, bounces up and keeps going into some forsaken black aural field. Blaring and unrecognizable, a roaring new battle flag.

John starts yelling. It sounds like one long open syllable, nothing but vowel, until he takes a breath and lets fly again.

"Generalissimo!" he yells, drawing out the o for as long as his Camel Filterless lungs allow. You and the Donalds start yelling too. You dig into the grocery bag. You light dozeners and throw. The roof is holding on again. It wants you and the ground can go to hell. Light and throw, light and throw and yell.

The chins respond, but they're out of their big guns. They shoot pathetic singular bottle rockets. They are ignorant of the dozener. Their volleys don't even threaten Kit, who is now running a steak knife up and down the fret, screaming on.

You send a dozener across the street that breaks apart over the chins' front yard with impeccable timing. Twelve cheap but angry little warheads scream earthward, sending khaki shorts and tucked-in shirts scattering in a beautiful strobe of white light and other people's fear. Pop. Pop pop pop pop.

Lost in the Bush[1]

nick johnson

[1] The title is something I changed for better or worse[A]. Otherwise this essay from Chuck's freshman composition class is exactly as I found it, except of course for the footnotes (and the research behind them) which I have supplied in an attempt to shed light on the shadowy nature of my cousin's life after he began working at Outback Steakhouse and was befriended by the bodybuilders working there. I never knew Chuck all that well, but he was much loved by our family and his disappearance has affected us deeply. If I intended to accomplish anything by going to and spending some time in the town[B] where he lived and worked prior to his disappearance, I suppose it was just to get to know him a little better. So then, let this be a testament of my affinity for someone with whom I share some blood.

It should also be noted—it's only fair to Chuck—that this essay, however waywardly it reads, was to be on the nature of freedom. I met with

[A] Chuck's original title "Experiencing Freedom" seems an obvious attempt to fool his instructor into thinking that freedom is the topic of the essay when it only marginally is, and for this reason and not the fact that his title is dull, I thought long and hard about a title that would speak to the true spirit of the essay.

[B] Danbrook, Louisiana, pop. 54,899. Located in the southwest corner of the state, this small city boasts bull-riding, water-skiing, bass fishing and alligator hunting as just a few of the sports it has

Chuck's composition instructor, a young graduate student by the name of Laurie Stubbs, who told me the prompt for the essay was to "write a narrative about the time in your life in which you felt the most free." Stubbs, who seemed genuinely fond of the essay, gave it a B+ because, as she explained it, the essay only vaguely addresses its topic. She was quick to remember Chuck as a shy and contemplative guy who generally avoided participation but possessed a warm personality. She also recalled (with some distress) the massive amounts of muscle that had found their way into my cousin's physique over the course of the semester.

to offer, making it a fine example for the state whose motto is Sportsman's Paradise. Fortunately, I found the town offers much more than that: it possesses true southern hospitality, something I'd only ever heard about, hailing from Vermont. Even with the solemn purpose of my visit, I couldn't resist the charm of the people. I found them categorically easy-going and talkative and only too ready to provide me with the facts of Chuck's life and the possible reason for his disappearance. It became apparent that many people in the area, perhaps in their passion for sports, harbored a deep respect for bodybuilders. Consequently, the newspaper and local news ran almost as many stories on Chuck's disappearance (despite his Yankee origins) as they did on the remodeling of the mayor's home, and everyone who learned I was his cousin wanted to furnish me with something to assist me in my search. I turned down offers of cars, trucks, boats, cell phones, .22 rifles, soft-shell crabs, places to sleep. One man offered me the use of his twin engine plane. When I told him I didn't know how to fly, he insisted on teaching me, promising that so long as I was careful I wouldn't need a license. He desisted only after I told him I didn't think I would be able to find what I was looking for from the sky. This abundance of hospitality and generosity was my saving grace, for the fact is I found the town and whole area unpredictable and untamed and I was not entirely happy about being there. It's true it was my idea to make the trip. No one asked me to. I just thought it was the least someone in the family could do in light of Uncle Roger's grief. He was so shaken by the news of his son's disappearance he pretty much slipped into a fog. He stopped communicating except to talk to the Danbrook Police whenever they called to update him, not that any of the updates had new information, though you wouldn't know it from Uncle Roger's expression as he listened, the way he hung on every word. What I found unnerving about the place was its aura of lawlessness. You could feel it in the people. The police detectives I spoke to seemed to take pride in their jobs and eager to enforce the law if they could see a law being broken, and people seemed genuinely saddened by Chuck's disappearance, but no one was adequately shocked by my cousin's disappearance. It was as if the onus was on Chuck to make himself reappear and if he couldn't, well, that sure would be a terrible pity. You got the feeling that nothing was stable, nothing permanent—laws along with people could disappear overnight and no one would ask any questions the next day.

WORKING AT OUTBACK STEAKHOUSE[2] is the best thing that has ever happened to me. It isn't just the family feeling you get, or the parties they throw outside work, or the half-price discount on the great Australian food. These things are great, but it's more than that. If I hadn't starting working there, I wouldn't have ever met Rusty[3] and the other bodybuilders[4], and I'd still be as puny today as I was six months ago. But it's not just being more muscular. Life I know now has more important things to offer that you can't touch. I've obtained self-respect both at work and at the gym. That's what Rusty does. That's what he's all about. When I was just me before working at Outback, I was just slipping around on life like it was an icepatch. Now this is no longer true. Each day that Rusty and me work together helps me. "Hey cousin, what did you eat today?" he'll say, pinching my side to monitor my fat. Rusty's got an eagle-eye for fat and the way people are. I know it's an exaggeration, but if Rusty was in charge of the world, the people in it would look a lot better, and they would be much happier.

When Rusty first took me under his wing, it was different. He had me putting away all the calories, fat included. I ate off a lot plates that female customers didn't finish. Rusty explained it all.

---

[2] A nationally franchised restaurant chain, with an Australian theme. The unwary customer will find plenty of heavy American food with catchy Australian names meant to convince him that he's getting a taste of the real "Down Under."

[3] Rusty Myers: Born July 2nd, 1970, Nome, TX. The oldest of the bodybuilders working at Outback at the time my cousin lived in Danbrook, Rusty was both Chuck's mentor and closest friend and generally regarded as the spiritual leader of these young men.

[4] This group of men who referred to themselves as "the Scientists" fragmented shortly after the Shreveport Incident[c] and went on to compete successfully in amateur bodybuilding.

> [c] What I have taken to calling the Shreveport Incident is the probable catalyst for my cousin's disappearance although there is no proof, and the police had almost no leads. More on this later.

"Only eat off of a babe's plate. Don't eat off no man's plate. Say she's cute, has a nice rack and she left half a rib-eye, you eat that shit, cousin! You eat all that shit, you hear! And it's gonna taste better knowing that some fine babe was eating on it. You hear, cousin! You'll see!"

And he was right. Like when a woman with big soft tits hadn't finished her rack of lamb I took her plate to the kitchen, found myself a little corner and pulled off one of the ribs and got the spicy smell of the meat in my nose and I thought, God, those tits were big and gushy. Big invincible tits like that make my stomach go slack. I guess I just relax when I see tits that big. I remember Rusty was going by just when I was eating that lamb. "Hey, Rusty," I called, "man, the lady who was eating on this has the best jugs of all time!" I couldn't keep the lamb juice from squirting out of my mouth. "Go, man, go!" he yelled. He had a thirty-five pound tray of steaks balanced on his hand and a couple of those steaks were headed to more babes. A lot of fine women eat here at Outback, which is another nice thing. Like when a pretty girl with big tits gets sat, her waiter will come in the kitchen and shout, "Big tits on 21!" Then every waiter in the house will eventually make his way over.

The waitresses and hostesses here are good looking too and everyone can pretty much sleep with everyone, except I'm not sleeping with anyone because Rusty doesn't think it's a good idea[5]. "You got to build up your testosterone, cousin. Plus, you'll get too many colds and shit from these girls. The pussy here spreads just a little bit too far, if you get my

---

[5] Can one man's persuasion of another not to sleep with women ever be viewed as on the up-and-up? Personally, it makes no difference to me if Rusty and Chuck had had sexual relations. But in light of the Shreveport Incident, it might be helpful to know the full extent of their relationship. Everyone is aware of the gay bodybuilder phenomenon and while Chuck's words signal something suspicious to me I could find nothing else to suggest that Rusty's motive was sexual, or rather, homosexual. Perhaps Rusty's philosophy is earnest and can be attributed to an egocentricity manifested in his need to coerce as many men as possible into a life of pumping iron, thereby validating his own way of life. A kind of the-more-bodybuilders-in-the-world-the-better rationale.

meaning. I'm not telling you what to do, I'm just recommending if you want to maintain peak performance then stay away from the pussy." Rusty is one of the smartest guys I know[6]. Cecil[7] and Alex[8] are pretty smart too. They lift weights and sometimes we lift in pairs. We're all partners, me and Rusty and Cecil and Alex. We're kind of like an Outback within Outback. Our own little family. We watch eachother's backs. Like with this problem with the guys from Shreveport[9]. They want to hurt Rusty because they say he rigged that bodybuilding competition in Shreveport. What a load of bull! He won it fair and square. Rusty is just one of the biggest, most ripped[10] guys in Louisiana. People have got to come to terms with that. Sure, their guy in Shreveport[11] is pretty big too, maybe as big and ripped as Rusty, but it was close enough to have gone either way. But they're saying Rusty paid the judges off. With what is what I want to know? Where is a waiter supposed to get the kind of money to pay

---

[6] I'm in no position to pass judgment on Chuck's perception for the intelligence of others. Rusty seems to have excelled in organic chemistry, math, and nutrition, but had difficulty with English, history and philosophy. Pertinent, however, about Chuck's assertion is that it shows his admiration for Rusty, a fact worth remembering in light of the Shreveport Incident.

[7] Cecil Aberdie. Born, May 19th, 1972, Monroe, LA. The biggest of "The Scientists," Cecil reputedly grew up on hog's milk, an idea implemented by his father, who dreamed of his son one day playing defensive end for the Saints.

[8] Alex Lementti. Born, June 2nd, 1975, New Orleans, LA. Due to an abnormally low percentage body fat went on to win more amateur titles since Mayfield's incredible run in the 70's.

[9] Over forty contestants appeared in the competition Rusty won, and while I was able to obtain a list of the names, I was unable to ascertain the names of those who had allegedly made threats on Rusty's arm.

[10] A physical condition of possessing dangerously low levels of body fat is reached through weight-lifting and extreme dieting and results in the bodybuilder's muscle to appear sharp and striated under the skin.

[11] George Huggins. Born March 11th, 1968, Shreveport, LA. As big as Rusty but not as big as Cecil, Huggins never quite achieved the low body mass index required to win competitions. He now does roof-contracting in Alexandria.

off judges? And now these Shreveport guys are threatening to do to Rusty what happened to Lance Mayfield[12]. The thing with us is that we've been warned and we're ready for them. Between Cecil and Alex and myself one of us is always with Rusty, like a bodyguard. It's been like this for a couple of weeks now. Because we know they're going to make their

---

[12] Lance Mayfield was the progenitor of the "Muscle-Shuffle," a unique form of flexing in which the contestant flexes upper and lower body parts while actually shuffling across stage, thereby passing in front of and showing up his competition. Mayfield held eleven championships before meeting with tragedy in Alabama. Critics attribute Mayfield's many state victories to his innovative flexing style, which was eventually outlawed in 1982 at which time Mayfield's winning streak came to an end, and at which point many critics argue he did in fact attempt to rig the Montgomery show, although no official ruling ever reflected as much.

Victim to one of amateur bodybuilding's most heinous acts, Mayfield was abducted and taken to some woods on the outskirts of Montgomery where his left arm was removed with a mechanical pipe-cutting saw[D]. Mayfield now resides in Southern Michigan where he delivers sermons at the Church of the Grace of Our Lord. For several months following the loss of his arm, Mayfield remained in a semi-state of shock. As part of his recovery, doctors encouraged him to pursue tennis, fencing, and a few other one-handed oriented sports but after finding he was physically too lop-sided to play any game enjoyably he turned to religion.

> [D] That some bodybuilders in Shreveport would even consider duplicating this depraved act on Rusty illustrates not only the lengths to which some will go in the fiercely competitive world of bodybuilding, it also gives credence to the prejudice that men who build muscle solve problems by muscle.
>
> There is little doubt that the punishment meant for Rusty was mistakenly carried out on Chuck. Even the police agree. Chuck, along with Cecil and Alex, was playing bodyguard to Rusty, and it seems as though they were all genuinely edgy over the prospect of the Shreveport bodybuilders giving them a visit. Rusty had even sought counseling at the university to deal with the prospect of losing his arm. Then, on the 17th of April, one week after Chuck wrote this essay, he and Rusty drove together to work in Rusty's truck. However, at the end of their shifts Rusty wanted to play Nintendo at Alex's, so he gave Chuck the keys to his truck, and that was the last anyone ever saw of my cousin. Rusty's truck was found in Rusty's driveway, the driver door wide open, the engine having idled until the gas ran dry. The police believe Chuck never returned home. It seems whoever was sent to hurt Rusty knew what he drove but not what he looked like. The question that nags at me is if it was the Shreveport bodybuilders and they did come to remove an arm, why wasn't Chuck's arm just cut off? Why has he vanished altogether?

move any day. For instance, two nights ago I switched shifts with Angie so I could do back-of-house duties with Rusty. Back-of-house is always last one out. So we left together and I followed him in my car to his apartment, which he shares with Cecil, where he's safe.

On our way home Rusty pulled off to the side of the road. At first I thought engine trouble but as soon as I'm out of my car I could hear his truck idling and when I got to him he was just sitting there, holding the wheel, staring into space.

When I asked him what was wrong he didn't even answer me. He just blinked and I thought maybe he was imagining his arm being cut off, like he was having this extended fantasy about it, and I told him I wouldn't let any such thing happen to him. He's been too good to me for me to let something like that happen. But maybe it wasn't much comfort. Maybe when you have arms as big as Rusty's the thought of having one cut off just paralyzes you. Like an arm that big is just so much of you, you can't imagine not having it and sometimes you almost wonder with arms so large if each one has its own brains and dreams. When you get ideas like that then you can see why he's got good reason to be upset.

"Don't you think we should move on, Rusty?"

"Man, I don't know what to do."

"What's the feeling, Rusty? What's the feeling, big guy?"

But Rusty wasn't talking. I went around to the passenger side and got in. I don't think he even noticed, which was all right. I wasn't in any hurry to get home. I'm always wide-awake when I get off work. When I get off work and walk out to my car I feel like the world is split right in half and I'm strolling through its liquid black center, running my hands over its gears. Of course all that sounds a little crazy and I wouldn't dare tell anyone at work about it. Like the time I told everyone how I figured out how McDonald's proudly serves child molesters[13]. It was a whole argument I made up in the car on the way to work. I was telling a few people in the kitchen and bunch of

[13] I'd really like to know where this came from; it really seems to say something about Chuck. But what?

others gathered around. I went something like this. "Okay, let's say there are 500,000,000 U.S. citizens. If 5% are regular customers at McDonald's and there are 10,000 McDonald'ses, each McDonald's sees 250 customers on a regular basis.

"Now if child molesters are predominantly men and 1% of the male population are child molesters, then there are two and half million child molesters in our country. So, since child molesters need to eat too and 5% of them are regular customers at McDonald's, then 12 child molesters eat regularly at each McDonald's."

Finally, I told everyone, "If McDonald's serves all their customers proudly, which we all know they do (it's policy) and child molesters are customers, then each McDonald's proudly serves 12 child molesters regularly."

By then our manager was listening too and when I was done he took me aside and told me he did not like the sound of my argument one bit and said if I ever speculated on how many child molesters ate at Outback he would fire me and maybe even have me sued for something. When I got home that night I figured it out. I couldn't help myself. You always end up doing those things you're forbid not to do. But I won't tell him I figured it out because I want to keep working there. I won't tell anyone because everyone gossips and knows everything and with information like that no one can be trusted. How do I now if I tell Jeff he won't tell Marci and it won't work its way back to the manager? You don't know. You can't. So now I know how many child molesters eat here. I just don't know which ones they are.

Still, the manager's message was loud and clear. Don't talk about anything unusual, talk only about things people are already talking about, go to the waiter section of your mind and you'll find appropriate things to say, talk about the ass on our newest hostess[14] or talk about David's mom's tits,

---

[14] The only instance of Chuck's sarcasm here, he must have felt bitterly over the infringement of what he was allowed to say, or at least felt strongly about the sexism and the pressure to conform in the environment of a theme-restaurant.

which even the hostesses agree hold up very nicely for a forty-year-old. David's mom[15] comes into the restaurant quite a bit, sits at the bar drinking vodka tonics. She's had sex with four waiters and I hear she's ready to have sex with more except I'll have to resist her because of my bodybuilding. Though I have to confess, when some of the guys invited me to go in on a gangbang I was tempted. They all paid some woman who lived down in Devil's Elbow[16] to let them do her at the same time, just so they could see what a gangbang was like. I guess the woman was real nice and they all

---

[15] When I came to town, Allison Vanders was still hanging on the bar at Outback, nursing vodka tonics. Chuck was right about her being well endowed. He didn't, however, mention how attractive she is. Perhaps a different sort of upbringing prevents me from writing with Chuck's candor, but I would be cowardly to hide the fact that Allison and I got together a number of times. Without too much detail, she came to my table one day while I was eating a ribeye and said, 'So you're the one who's been asking all the questions.' We ended up at her apartment and by morning I developed a little crush on her. I remember the moment vividly. She was wearing a red tee-shirt and lemon-yellow panties, sitting cross-legged on her carpet in front of the TV with a cigarette in her mouth and a Steven Seagal movie in her hand, asking me if I wanted to watch it or not. She was nuts about Seagal, and that was eye opening for me because I assumed all women over the age of 30 either didn't know of Seagal or couldn't stand him. The smoke was scaling the side of her face and she had this vague smile as she waited for me to respond, and I think she liked me but wondered how long I would stay with her. I had somehow gathered that the guys from Outback who'd bedded her did it only as a joke, and I think she knew this at some level and was wondering if I had done it as a joke too even if I wasn't one of the waiters. And then in a flash I wanted to do whatever I could to secure her and make her interested in me forever. Really nothing more than a fleeting fantasy, it didn't happen. But I did like her very much.

[16] Not particularly sinister, Devil's Elbow is an especially sharp crook in Lower Base Bayou where six-time speedboat champion, Rex Heffler, ran aground at 112 mph so that both body and boat disintegrated upon interfacing with the Louisiana local hardwoods there onshore.

Locals with a belief in the supernatural claim that if you stand on the bridge near the Elbow you can hear the high-pitched scream of Heffler's Mercury inboard/outboard running at 8000 rpm intermittently through the night. Others maintain the sound to be merely that of insects and water fowl.

had a lot of fun. She let them do her in the butt[17], and the whole thing boiled down to them pulling out real fast just to watch her butthole close up. And I can see how that would be pretty fun. At first, they said it would stay open as big as a half-dollar and inside it was the color of one of our sirloins cooked mid-rare. When they told me that though I thought to myself how small-minded they were, that all they can really think about is steaks and GSBs[18]. That's not who I am. I like my job, but I can think about things, and make things up out of nothing and this is a gift, and it doesn't mean I wished I hadn't been in on the fun with the woman at Devil's Elbow because she sounds real sweet to take on so many sex-hungry guys. I just know I've got to be different. And if Rusty and Cecil and Alex weren't working at Outback I might not've hung around so long. Now my arms and legs and chest are bigger. I eat better and people don't mess with me even if they think I am different. But I'm just smarter.

But all of that is beside the point in a way.

Sitting there in Rusty's truck I noticed a ticking. At first I couldn't find the source of it, then I saw it was the clock on his dashboard getting on to 1 a.m.

"We've got to lift in the morning, Rusty."

"I know, cousin."

"You're just worrying over this whole Shreveport thing."

---

17 Initially I assumed that this anal fixation seemed to cut against Outback Code and its family-oriented menu, but the more I interviewed the food servers at store Z4545 the more I understood how their interest in anal-related sex was surprisingly innocent and wholesome. Analingus seemed to be very much on the mind of the male food server, and nearly every female food server had admitted to having inserted her finger in the rectum of at least one of the male food servers. What became clear is that the employees at this restaurant like to live life to the fullest. Perhaps one male food server put it best: "Outback is a place for fun, and that's all! You don't have inhibitions here, and if you do, you don't last too long. Now let's get shit-faced!" I'm sure shit-faced here means drunk and nothing more. The Outback staff was not big on wordplay.

18 Grilled Shrimp on the Barbie, Outback's second-most popular appetizer. Six frozen jumbo shrimp grilled over an open gas flame, displayed on a rectangle of seasoned honey wheatberry toast and served with two lemon wedges and a ramekin of remoulade.

"I'm a non-violent mother fucker," said Rusty. "I mean people think you lift weights so you can bust heads, or so that people won't bust yours. That's stupid people, man!"

"I know it, Rusty."

"Stupid people don't know about guys like you and me. They don't understand the beauty of the body. The science of eating! The science of eating, man!"

"That's us, Rusty."

"My body is a temple. The Greeks understood that, right, Chuck? Isn't that what you said one time?"

"It's the truth, Rusty. The Greeks were holy people. That's why they raised so many chickens and pigs[19]. They knew how to eat."

"But they were fighters too," Rusty said.

"Only because times were different. If we had a Greek guy with us today, he would be at the gym lifting with us tomorrow. We'd have him eating egg whites and potatoes and ketchup and playing Nintendo with us at night."

"Except they were big wine drinkers, and I can't abide by that."

"But their wine was practically grape juice, Rusty. It doesn't count."

Rusty hung his head. He looked tired and worried.

"This thing'll blow over, Rusty. You'll see. Those Shreveport guys, they're not coming down here. And if they do, we just gotta take care of it, right?"[20]

---

[19] It's hard to know exactly where Chuck got this idea. He hadn't taken any classics courses, nor are the Beasley's particularly familiar with mythology. Based on the loose logic that a people are holy because they raise pigs and chickens, I will propose that Chuck either made this up or misremembered something that at one point did make sense to him. And yet all of that pales in importance when I consider that the topic seems to have meant something almost spiritual to Rusty and Chuck.

[20] Chuck, of course, had no idea what taking care of it would ultimately require. His words, so innocent, ring of a worst-case scenario in which the bodybuilders of Z4545 face off against the Shreveport bodybuilders in a Westside Story-style brawl in Outback's parking lot. Chuck gets in a lick or two before a punch to his gut takes him nobly out of the fight. Maybe the

"Right."

"All right!" I said. I gave him a square punch in the shoulder. It's like hitting a rhino.

I went back to my car, got in, and started it. I like working at Outback and doing bodybuilding with Rusty and Cecil and Alex. Even if I never get to be as big as those guys, I figure I'm happy now. I feel like I've reached a kind of rest stop and I can stay as long as I want and the State Trooper won't come by and kick me out. That's because I have achieved independence in my life. When you're a kid you need your family but you don't choose them, and even if you've got a good family, you get to a point where you can choose the people you need and be happy needing the people you choose, and what better example of freedom is there?

---

highlight is someone getting thrown through the windshield of a pickup. But the whole thing ends anticlimactically, tapering off the way some fights do, in a mutually silently acknowledged draw, both sides feeling they've made their points with their dignities intact. But, then, this scenario is the product of my imagination, not Chuck's. It's how I see the conflict playing itself out back in good, upstanding Vermont, as though such extreme and violent remedies that include dark woods and mechanical saws are particular to this backwards place. But I don't know this place well enough to cast such judgement. For all I know, it is Chuck who possessed extremity and violence, for I have to face the fact that I've learned very little about my cousin's state of mind here. How can I be sure he didn't change in some crucial way? Maybe the place changed him. Listening to Laurie Stubbs describe him, I would never recognize him. So who am I to say what his words ring of? I've no way of knowing if Chuck is even anything like the boy he was from our childhood summers in St. Johnsville. And I must be resigned to the possibility that I will never know.

I learned very little in my interview of Rusty, whom I met only once. He made it clear that he was not interested in going over what he called old history. We stood facing each other in the parking lot of his gym where I tracked him down as he was leaving. A summer storm was threatening to break over our heads, the wind seemed to be blowing vertically and Rusty seemed anxious to get home. He was an enormous man, at least six feet tall and upwards of 250 lbs. His red hair was cropped close to his scalp in an attempt to diminish the fact that he was going bald. He wore a pair of tiny wire-frame glasses that squeezed his face so hard his temples were caught in a perpetual isometric exercise. From reading Chuck's essay I was forewarned of Rusty's charisma, if that is in fact the word.

Three Lessons in Firesurfing

anne elliott

The crit starts in the foundry courtyard, where Patrick Larsen's steel "thing" keeps growing. I've noticed Patrick tends to work without a plan. But he shows up at 9 a.m. sharp every day, pours black coffee from his thermos, puts on his welding mask, and sets to work. Adding more and more rusty steel crap to this giant, heroic but essentially shapeless amoeba made of I-beams and rods and discs. He breaks at 11:30 for lunch, from a metal lunchbox, teamster style. After eating, he picks his teeth, smokes a cigarette, walks around the piece. Then puts his mask back on. Sparks fly steadily until 4 o'clock. Beer Time. Turns off the welder, puts leftover rods and mask and gloves neatly in his locker.

I share the thought. "I find Patrick's process interesting. His work habits. He has a punctuality. A routine, I guess. Almost like a portrait of the American work ethic."

Patrick chews his afternoon toothpick thoughtfully, scruffy blonde beard framing a half-smile. He seems to appreciate the comment. Steve Pak, dressed in head-to-toe big-city black, disagrees. “Come on, Sara. Can you really see that in the *work*? His *habits*? Why not talk about the *piece*? That’s what we’re here to critique.”

Steve intimidates me terribly. Huge vocabulary. Works hard. Knows every sculptor who ever lived. BFA from the Art Institute of Chicago, full ride fellowship here. The rest of us have “graduate assistantships,” cleaning undergrad studios and maintaining equipment, filing shit for Professor O’Malley.

O’Malley, we call him *Boss*. It fits him. He’s a big ruddy guy with big arms and a big truck. I think he has a big brain too, but I’m not sure yet. Mostly I just see him collecting money for beer. Today’s our first crit of the year. My first year. My first chance to hear him for real.

“I’m with Steve,” says Boss with frank authority. “We can talk about process, sure, but would you really see this ‘work ethic’ if this piece was in a gallery?”

I give in. “No, I suppose not.” Actually, I hate the piece, but was trying to keep it positive.

“So, look at the *work*, Sara,” Boss pushes. “What is it giving you?”

“It’s giving ME the HIVES,” interjects Karla Wells, nearly kicking it with one of her steel-toed boots.

“You’ll have your chance, dear,” says Boss, pulling her away from it by her tattooed arm. She glares angrily at the blob of steel, at its creator.

“I’m not exactly sure what it’s *giving* me,” I mutter, ready to pass the buck.

“There’s kind of an architectonic thing happening over here,” offers Mary Sark, our token ceramicist, crouching on the cement floor, pointing with a dirty fingernail.

“See, I think it’s more biomorphic,” says John Truman. John should know biomorphic. His sculptures are literally alive with fungus. “I like the tension he’s created between these two massive verticals.” He squints up at it through his nerdy wireframe glasses. “Reminds me of the crotch of a tree."

"Or the CROTCH of SOMEONE," Karla Wells snorts, perpetual cigarette dangling from her lip, her muscular arms akimbo in her battered tank tee, battle position.

"*Excuse* me?" Patrick says, actually puffing out his ample chest.

"Dear MOM, I miss your STEELY THICK THIGHS," Karla spews.

"*Mom*?" Patrick only has one syllable in defense.

"Hey, that's what the work is GIVING ME," Karla retorts, pale chin up.

The crit has gotten off to a lovely start.

Karla's a force field. I met her my first day here, in my studio, unpacking my sewing machine and fabric and books. She wandered in, without knocking.

"Hey."

"Hey."

She is wearing what I will soon learn is her uniform: wifebeater undershirt, no bra, crew cut slicked back with pomade, nose ring, worn men's jeans, and boots covered in paint and resin. She's a big person. Six feet tall.

"I'm Karla." Holding her hand out like a man for a shake.

"Sara."

"I know. I saw your slides." She's second year, got a say in our selection. "Fiber artist."

"Well..." I say, not crazy about the label. "Let's just say *artist*."

"You're not a *painter*," she says, poking through some raw wool I put out on the table earlier.

It's The Test, her question, the one I'll take again and again while I'm here. "Strictly 3-D for me."

"Good. I hate painters. Paintings are what you back into when you're looking at sculpture." I passed the test, at least for now. "You know, I voted for you," she confides. "I've had enough of this macho steel shit." She lights a cigarette, without asking. I don't smoke. I hate it, but I dare not object.

Maybe she will become a real ally. I am going to need one.

"What kind of stuff do you do?" I ask. I hand her an empty soda can for an ashtray. She flicks onto the floor anyway.

"Polyester resin." It's a point of pride among some sculptors, working with horribly toxic materials. Macho in its own way, but I don't say it. "And tampons, lately. *Used* ones," with a twinkle in the eye intended for me. The extra X chromosome is an asset here, perhaps. Or, realistically, an obstacle.

The crit moves into Steve Pak's space, just off the woodshop. He's first year too, but you wouldn't know it. He has at least ten objects arranged on the floor, in a spiral. They're heavy, fruitlike, rounded, carved from large hunks of wood. I watch him sometimes in the courtyard, going at an oak stump with a chain saw. It's a loud process. I doubt he even notices me watching his wordless, meditative focus on the wood, as if he doesn't even hear the saw. He works fast, but mindfully, paying attention to knots, often leaving them intact. He leaves bark in places. But then, back in his studio, he coats the pieces with metal cladding. Copper and bronze mostly, some aluminum, affixed with hundreds of little nails. He leaves the wood surface selectively, sometimes on the inside of a gourdlike form, meticulously sanded and oiled to bring out the grain. It's hard to resist the urge to touch them.

"Okay, who's going to start?" Boss breaks the silence, the respect and jealousy evident on all our faces. It's hard to know where to begin.

"I love how the cladding here echoes the bark on this other piece," offers Mary the Ceramicist.

"There's a real respect for the materials," I say. I notice Karla has given in to the urge and has begun stroking the soft wood on the inside of one of the forms.

"Can you elaborate?" Boss pushes. Steve stands silent. Critique etiquette, waiting for responses. He doesn't seem nervous at all. Hands in the pockets of his black jeans, fully present, listening. Pushing his long black hair from his face, around an ear.

"Well, I don't know." Again I am tongue-tied.

John Truman rescues me. "Well, like Mary said, it's imitative. Like the copper over here, it imitates the rough bark over there. But it's not trying to be anything but copper. The copper is copper, the bark is bark. But they also comment on each other."

"Good," Boss replies. "But let Sara finish her thought."

"That's it. What he said. That's my thought." Boss looks me in the eye, waiting for more. Steve Pak looks at me like I'm absolutely stupid.

"How did you get this patina?" Karla is touching a part of the copper that has been blackened, but not really. The black has tinges of blue. The surrounding wood looks a little burnt, the patina feathering naturally from the metal.

"That one, just a propane torch," Steve says. Just a propane torch, like it's nothing. Obviously there's some technique to his application. We are all taking mental notes. Figuring out what we can steal without looking like we are stealing. He takes an unintentional glance at a plastic jug of some liquid suspended from the ceiling, a slow drip engineered overhead, a bright green patina growing on the pointy copperized tip of the form beneath it, spreading slowly and elegantly from its center.

"What's in that jug?" says Karla without hesitation, voicing the thought we are all having. "Ammonia? It smells like ammonia."

"Ancient Korean secret," winks Steve.

"You won't share the recipe?" laughs Boss, not wanting him to.

Steve just smiles, basking in Boss' approval.

Steve is a hard act to follow, and due to the proximity of my space, I'm the lucky one. I have only one piece to share and it's not big. It's on a table in the middle of my space. I cleaned up a bit, last night, put unused materials in boxes against the wall. The piece looks lonely and tiny in the middle of the room now, a far cry from the collective awe we felt in Steve's studio.

I've been getting into felt lately. It's such a magic process. Just a little soapy water and manipulation and the wool shrinks and thickens. I've discovered it hardens and dries nicely around objects, which is my main experiment now. I made a good sized felt bowl, then filled it with felted objects I brought in from home. Important objects, to me, like an old sketch journal, or a kitchen timer my mother gave me, or a framed photograph. I shroud each object in the natural-colored wool, then submerge them in a soapy bath, one by one, and let the materials take over.

Karla has helped herself, picking up the kitchen timer, shaking it to figure out what's the heavy thing inside. "It's okay," I say, breaking the critique code. "You can handle them. I want you to."

Everyone follows orders, inspecting the little things, passing them around. "Well," says John, "there is the obvious comparison to Steve's work. The fiber is almost like the cladding. A coating of a contrasting material."

"True," says Boss.

"And the contrast of the weights of the different objects. I like that," says Mary, hefting the journal.

"My hands are getting greasy," Karla says, setting her object down, wiping her palms on her pants.

"That's the lanolin of the wool," Steve says.

"How do we react to that?" asks Boss. "The fact that she's asked us to touch them, and they are spreading oil on our hands? Is it a dirty trick?"

"I'm not crazy about it," says Patrick. "What if you were allergic?"

"ARE you allergic?" counters Karla.

"No, I'm just saying."

The crit is getting offtrack, I feel. I decide to steer it back where it belongs. "The objects are precious," I say. "They're personal objects from my life. Like this one, it's a rag doll from my childhood. And here is a photo of my brother."

"But I don't know that. I can't *see* the photo," Steve says, clearly disappointed in me for speaking, for not letting the work do the talking.

"But it's still true," I say, feeling a blush coming.

"This one is personal too?" says John, waving a shrouded toilet plunger in the air with a laugh. I've lost my footing. I'm the target now.

"Yes, it's personal." I resist the urge to grab it from his hand.

"Why does it matter to you so much? The source of the objects?" Boss says.

"Look," I say, feeling anger in my belly. "Like Steve's stuff. It's obvious he loves his wood and copper and whatever the hell is dripping from that patina thing. How is this any different?"

Boss is cool, but not letting me off the hook. "But you're focused on *backstory.* You hit the nail on the head. It's *obvious* Steve's in love with his materials. It's just not coming through here. You actually have to give us the information."

"What, you mean like stand next to it and explain? Write it out?"

"No, of course not. That's not what I mean. You think about it. We need to move on. Any last comments?"

"I don't think it's finished yet," Steve says. I can't tell if it's encouragement or an insult.

"It's all one color," says Patrick. "Can't you dye the wool, maybe give the piece more variety? More of a visual clue?"

I am communicating nothing here. "I could, if I wanted to," I say.

"But you don't WANT to," says Karla, my lone defender.

"No, I don't." I can't look anyone in the eye.

I'm rattled. It's hard to concentrate and contribute now. In Mary's space, we see a collection of coil-built female figures, whimsical, unfired, all brown clay, but no one complains about it being monochromatic. And John's towers of fungus, tall, skinny, phallic, their stench assaulting our nostrils. No one complains of the smell being a dirty trick. No comments about allergies. I find myself holding my tongue. My opinion will only be shot down, judged. There is no point.

Karla's space is big, and messy as hell. Packrats are common in the sculpture world, but this borders on mania. Boxes, milk crates of crap everywhere, under tables, on top of them, a half a dozen dirty electric fans, pieces of salvaged furniture leaned against the wall. She has a lot of light—four big windows—a requirement for ventilation when using resin. But the light fills her work too, her "aquariums," becomes one of the materials themselves.

It's been interesting to watch the aquariums evolve. For me, anyway. First she lays dozens of bloody tampons out on a table, like wedges of fruit, to dry. She puts a big fan on them, and sometimes a hairdryer propped up on a crate, to speed them along. I approached the table slowly the first time she invited me in. I thought it would smell horrible, the old blood, but it didn't. "I know what you're thinking," she said. "Once they're dry, they're practically the same as your hunks of wool. Hardly any smell. And look, they're kind of beautiful." Like beloved collector toys, the way she arranges and rearranges them on the table. "No two exactly alike."

I have to laugh. "Snowflakes, fingerprints, tampons..." I edge over and look at them. Almost like dried flowers, each with a little stem, meticulously arranged. "Hey, these are different," I say, pointing to a group with blue strings instead of white.

"You're very observant," she replies, in mock teacher mode. "I figured, why not change brands and see what happens?"

I notice a bushel basket of tampons, like dried plums, in the corner. "Damn, girl, maybe you should see a doctor. You bleed a lot."

She laughs, relieved that I am not calling her a freak. "Nah, people send 'em to me. My sister, some undergrad friends."

"Wow." I wonder if I will ever have the courage to make a donation. If mine will measure up to those of her friends. Probably lesbians too. Lesbians make me uneasy sometimes. I'm never sure how friendly I should get.

The crit ends in Karla's space. She's made a real effort to clean around four blocks of clear resin, under the windows, with tampons suspended inside them like swimming fish. They really are beautiful, and technically remarkable, the way she keeps the resin from getting too cloudy, and injects bubbles over some of the creatures as if they are breathing. Some of them facing each other, in little conversations. The sculptors all stand back, not close enough to really see the gesture and uniqueness of each swimming tampon. Karla is tense, chainsmoking on the edge of the group, slouching, waiting for someone to speak.

Mary is not afraid of it. She approaches, peers close. "It's whimsical. Random and not random. They remind me of sperm."

"I don't get it," says Patrick, sneering in disgust.

"Can you be more specific?" says Boss, tired now, a little squeamish himself, operating on rote.

"I don't get *why*. Why we should want to look at these things." Patrick can't even bring himself to name them.

"Why don't *you* want to look at them?" Boss says.

"Isn't it *obvious*?" He looks like he is going to be sick.

"But it's natural," I say, finally unable to keep quiet. "What could be more natural?"

"That?" Patrick points, his hand still an arm's reach from the nearest block. "*That* is not natural. Saving those things? Some things shouldn't be shared."

"But they *are* shared, YOU just don't share it," Karla accuses. "It's something HALF THE POPULATION recognizes intimately, right SARA? Right MARY? Why are YOU so afraid of it? IT'S NOTHING. LOOK." She digs into the bushel basket in the corner, brings up a handful of them, held by the strings, dangles them in Patrick's face like snakes. Taunting him as he backs right into Steve Pak.

He kicks at her in self defense. She throws the bouquet of tampons at his head. Some scrambling, yelling, and Boss grabs Karla by the waist as she tries to slap Patrick. Steve and John hold him back—he's big—until he cools down and brushes himself off, then faces her. Hatred in his Nordic blue eyes. "I'm outta here," he says, turns, adjusts his army jacket, leaves.

"Okay," says Boss, trying to resurrect the discussion. Karla fuming, stomping her boot on the concrete floor. Mary and I wordlessly, instinctively, do what women do, clean. We pick the tampons up from the floor, carefully, return them to the bushel basket.

The crit is definitely over.

I go to my studio, close the door, put Joni on the tape deck, volume high. Sit on the lone chair, looking at my stupid basket of stupid precious objects. *California, I'm coming home,* Joni sings with a clarity I wish I had. I miss home. I am not cut out for this. Whoever said Midwesterners were polite never had to deal with this lot.

Unfinished, Steve Pak called it. This experiment, full of so many hours, careful selection of mementos, sacrificing them for the piece, that sacrifice appreciated by no one but me. A lump of useless felt. A blob, no more meaningful than Patrick's steel monstrosity, which at least has scale going for it.

Unfinished. I'm pissed, because I know in my gut Steve is right. I'm looking at it now, and it doesn't move me. I hate it.

I grab a pair of scissors and begin stabbing at one of the objects on top. The kitchen timer. It slides around. I can't even stab it effectively. I pull it out of the bowl and begin cutting at the felt with the sharp shears, a surgical slice right over its heart, then around the top, releasing the object inside.

I'm surprised by what falls out of the skin onto my lap.

The timer now unrecognizable, nonfunctional, its old tin caked with rust. I never really considered this possibility. Far from protecting the thing inside, the skin of felt has changed it. And the skin itself is beautiful too, a perfect, rusty negative, a clue, a *story. Focused on backstory,* Boss complained, but this is different. Not backstory, but present tense. A new story. Here, now, free of nostalgia. Free.

Eagerly, I use the scissors to free the other objects. The ink from the journal has run onto the inside of the felt, pages buckled in a natural ripple. The wood of the picture frame is rotten. The photo, surreal colors now, has reacted with the detergent bath. The colors on the rag doll's face runny, like she is crying, the fibers of her hair and dress sticking now to the inside of her mold in a crosshatched pattern. I liberate all the objects, then lay the skins on one side of the table, opened like dissected frogs, and the transformed objects on the other side. I toss the felt bowl under the table. I don't need it now.

Joni stops singing. The tape is over. I hear music outside, something more hardcore, driving drums, tribal, people yelling and laughing. I take a last look at my table of specimens, turn off the light, and go outside to investigate.

Someone has lit a bonfire in the middle of the gravel parking lot. A cooler of beer sits on the tailgate of Boss' truck. Karla is feeding wood to the fire, broken furniture I recognize from her studio. Everyone is smoking and laughing, beer going down like water.

"Sara! Where have you been?" Boss says, opening me a bottle.

"Working."

"Good girl." He tousles my hair with his big rough hand. Then laughs from his belly, watching John and Patrick lay a plank of wood on the top of the fire. John, his nerdy glasses yellow in the firelight, stands rocking at the edge of the fire, then leaps, his boots gripping the rough plank, into the middle of the flame. He stands there for a moment, whooping and beating his chest like a gorilla before jumping to safety.

"You ever seen firesurfing before?" Boss asks.

"No. I can't say I have." I take a swig of the icy beer.

Patrick leaps onto the plank right after John. Sideways, legs apart, crouching for balance, like a true surfer. He lets out a lion's roar, leaps off, making a surge of sparks behind him. Boss, beside me, is cheering.

Karla lays another board and jumps onto it without hesitation, waving a stick overhead like a sword. Not to be outdone, Patrick jumps on after her, bottle of bourbon in his hand, releases mouthful into the air, sparkly in the firelight. "Oh yeah?" Karla says, full warrior now. "Watch THIS," and sets a wooden chair onto the board, sits on it like it's nothing, legs crossed demurely, stays a second too long for my comfort.

"Atta girl!" Boss shouts. "Show 'em how it's done."

There's an art to firesurfing, it seems. Caught up in the spirit, Mary and Steve, my fellow first-years, join the fray, jump onto the board together, hand in hand, half dare, half pas de deux. Some coaxing, and even Boss steps into the fire. This is crazy. He is over sixty. He could fall. I remind myself there is a fire extinguisher in the foundry courtyard.

"Sara, come on! It's fun!" goads Mary, pulling me by the hand. I'm terrified. My hair is long and flammable. I'm wearing sandals. She pulls me through the flames onto a piece of plywood. Sparks shoot up and all around us and heavy smoke and heat and orange make everything else invisible. I almost want to stay there, in the hot orange world.

"Go Sara!" I hear Boss shouting as Mary pulls me to safety. And a laugh from deep in my abdomen, pure giddiness and lightness and freedom.

"Wants some of my mushroom tea?" says John, appearing beside me with a pitcher and a stack of plastic cups. There's something different about him, a wildness in his eyes, behind his sparkling glasses, an internal fire, something animal.

"Sure." Hallucinogen, presumably. It tastes bitter. I sip

slowly. He downs a full cup, glug glug, wipes his mouth with his sleeve, skips off. I abandon the tea, return to my beer.

The feeling around the bonfire is changing. Karla throws on another board and jumps up and down on it, crushing live coals under her weight, wailing like a banshee. Patrick practically pushes her off, then balances on one foot. It's a contest now. Between Patrick and Karla, the latest battle in a long war. Karla jumps back on with a pitchfork, strikes an American Gothic pose until her jeans catch fire and she jumps off, slapping the flame down with her bare hand. Patrick again, with a cigarette in his mouth, does a goofy pirouette. Karla, fierce, hops on and lets fly a karate kick. It's getting out of hand, joyless and angry. Boss should take charge. Someone's going to get hurt. Unease and nausea in my empty gut.

Suddenly, John Truman comes dashing from the building, screaming wildly, waving his arms, wearing nothing but cowboy boots and white briefs, hair a sticky fright. We all stand agape as he sets a metal stool on the board and stands on top of it, arms overhead, his skinny body a gleaming white tower in the fiery fountain.

I wake up with something wet and rough touching my ear. And a horrible smell. Dog breath. Karla's pit bull, Louise Nevelson, is licking my face, burrowing and sniffing in my hair.

I crashed in my studio after the bonfire last night, too late to walk home alone, and everyone else way too fucked up to trust for a ride. I'm on the floor under my table, on top of a bunch of fabric and wool, my retired felt bowl a surprisingly comfortable pillow. Karla strides in, freshly showered and wide awake. "Hey! Hey! Are you ready?"

"Ready? Huh?"

"Today's our trip to government surplus."

"Oh yeah. I forgot." Louise the Dog is curling up beside me, as lazy as I feel.

"Hey, you cut open your felt things. This is cool. Look at

this rust."

"Yeah." I get up. Stretch. Sore back.

She surveys the skins on the table, and their liberated guts. Nods her head, smiles. "You may be onto something."

I hear voices and laughter in the courtyard. "Is there time for coffee?" I croak.

"C'mon. I got a thermos in my truck."

It's John riding with Patrick, Steve riding with Boss, and the girls bringing up the rear of the 3-pickup caravan. Louise Nevelson rides in the back of Karla's truck. Mary wedges between Karla and me in the cab. Karla's coffee is too sweet, but I drink it anyway, grateful. I'm the only one with any apparent hangover.

"What happened with John Truman last night?" Mary asks. We've reached the edge of town. Strip malls give way to corn fields, and flatness to the horizon, miles away. "Seriously. Jumping into the fire in his *underwear*?"

"He does that. He's an exhibitionist."

"I never would've guessed," muses Mary, shaking her auburn head.

"Last year, someone started calling him John Truman Capote."

"Ah," Mary laughs. "As in dweeby intellectual by day, world class hedonist by night?"

"I guess," Karla says with a shrug. "I never read him."

"Capote? Didn't you ever see *Breakfast at Tiffany's*?"

"Me?" Karla cackles. I say nothing. I can see Boss laughing ahead of us, probably at Steve Pak's wit. Damn teacher's pet.

Karla downshifts around a turn. "Mary, you gotta see what Sara did to her piece last night. She *dissected* it."

"Really?" Mary turns to me.

"Yeah," I say, not quite ready to talk about it yet. "Say, how far is this place?"

"About a hundred miles," Karla says in an exhale of smoke. "But don't worry. It goes fast. It's *coming back* that takes time."

I don't ask. The smoke assaults my sinuses as the flat Midwestern fall speeds by outside the window. Louise's pink snout, in the passenger side mirror, joyfully sniffs the clean country air.

The government surplus warehouse is a candy store for sculptors. Room after room of junk, dirt cheap to institutions. Circuit boards. Spools of wire. Plumbing supplies. Antiquated medical devices. All of us wide-eyed, not sure where to begin.

John gravitates to the chemistry gear: boxes of dusty 1950's era beakers and test tubes in racks. Patrick, Boss, and Steve are focused on a large, rusty, decommissioned propane tank. They can fight over who gets to cut it up, I don't care. Mary is fascinated by an old iron lung. Karla is checking out a pile of pink rubber tubing.

I find myself in a room full of uniforms, haphazardly folded on a table. Not just camouflage and military, but also lab coats, wetsuits, surgical scrubs. Maybe this is what I need: a proper uniform in which to *perform surgery* on my felt objects. I pick out a blue scrub suit, about my size, set it aside.

I find an old, felt park ranger's hat, green, like Smoky the Bear's, turn it over to examine its construction. The felt is much tighter and harder than the felt I have been making. The brim springs back after I bend it. I pop it on my head. There are no mirrors. I step up to the window separating my little room from the next one, fall in love with the hat on my head in the dusty reflection.

"Hey! You look like Joseph Beuys!"

I nearly jump out of my skin. It is Steve, peering through from the other side.

"Sorry. I didn't mean to startle you." He disappears, reappears in the room beside me. Begins trying on a lab coat. Then a flight suit. With a nurse's cap. Gleefully, like a kid playing dress-up, only on speed, he's shifting personalities rapidly and seamlessly. Dispensing with modesty, taking off his pants to try on a cop uniform. "Well, little lady, how fast do you think you were going?" Involving me in his game. I'm flummoxed. He's a different person. Swim fins and a gas mask. With a chef's apron. And a life preserver. Trying to get me to laugh. Some goofy safety glasses. He tosses me a pair. "Look!" In a paper hazmat suit and goggles, "I'm DEVO!"

I don't know what to say. Mr. Serious Teacher's Pet and Critique Etiquette prancing and squealing, with a four-year-old's energy and imagination. "Sara, check this! *Watches.* We can *synchronize* them for *Beer Time.*" A box of a dozen of them, white faces, green web bands, army issue. He puts the whole box on his pile. "Enough for *all of us*!"

I'm speechless, but his energy is contagious. "Oh. Oh. Sara. This one's yours. Definitely." He tosses me a red man's sleepshirt. I put it on over my clothes. "Yes!" he cries, handing me a khaki utility vest to put over it. It feels right. I look at my reflection in the window.

"What the hell?" Karla steps in to see what the commotion is. We must look ridiculous, Steve in the Devo ensemble, me dressed like a goofy hippy in nightshirt and vest and big-brimmed hat. She laughs explosively, shakes her head like a proud but befuddled parent, and leaves us alone to our impromptu performance.

"There's one rule of sculpture. If you can't make it *good*, make it *big*. If you can't make it *big*, make a *lot of 'em.*" Boss is drunk, dispensing his wisdom, holding court at the bar of a dirty dive called Smokey's, in a little town I think is called Springville. It's the third bar we've been to on our trip back. Now I know what Karla meant: *it's coming back that takes time.*

I'm tired. I look at my new army-issue watch: it's past midnight. I go to the other end of the bar, order another Stag beer. Watch Patrick from across the room, absorbing Boss' advice like gospel. Karla joins me. "Same old shit," she mutters, putting money on the bar.

"Yeah." I take a swig. Fortification.

Steve squeezes between us. "Joseph Beuys!" he says, tweaking my new felt hat. "I've been thinking about that. I don't know why I never thought of it before. The felt—you know how Beuys used felt because it *saved his life* during the war. Some peasants wrapped him in felt and fat, so it *became his material.*"

Karla, awakening now, grins. "You're right! Why didn't that come up in the crit?"

"But I've been thinking," Steve continues, his black eyes bright with epiphany. "That's what's missing in your piece. *You.* Like Beuys. You need to *be in it.* Forget wrapping stuff, what if you wrapped *yourself*? To see what it feels like? As an experiment? Then there would be no question about the personal aspect! You wouldn't have to explain anything!"

"Yeah!" Karla affirms, slamming her bottle on the bar.

I try to imagine it, logistically, creating the felt around my body. A bathtub full of detergent. I'll need help. Modesty will be out of the question. But the idea intrigues me. Like trying on a cop uniform, to see what it feels like. Trying on my work, to see what the objects feel. To transform myself, like the objects were transformed. To see the skin after it is removed. I smile. "Thanks, professor," I say.

"And *you,*" Steve says, pointing rudely, but not rudely, in Karla's face. "Talk about *involving the body.* You scared everybody! *Tampons*! The look on Patrick's face!" He laughs maniacally. "You scared *me*! I never seen those things before, bloody like that. *Damn.* But I like that! I like being scared. It's *power.*"

Karla looks down at him gratefully, a welcome warmth at this end of the bar, constructive and invigorating. "Really?"

"It makes me think." Steve, a little drunk, on a roll now. "You know? I admit I adore formalist stuff, but I'm in a rut. I wish I could be more like you guys. Really laying something on the line. Putting the *self* out there, you know? Like a true experiment." And the jealousy in his face genuine, like everyone else in his studio yesterday, all of us wanting just a little of his technical accomplishment. I'm humbled.

"Hey O'Malley!" The bartender, shouting to Boss. They are friends, from years and years of these sculptor's bar crawls. "I gotta joke for you. *A hippy, a Chink, and a dyke walk into a bar.*"

Silence. I realize he is looking at the three of us. I must be the hippy, still wearing the red nightshirt and khaki vest over yesterday's smelly clothes, my long hair streaming out under the Joseph Beuys hat. And Steve, the only Asian in the room—or indeed the whole town, probably—we know which one he is. All faces are frozen on the other end of the bar. Mary looks like she wants to die. Meanwhile Karla, the dyke, is red and might kill someone.

And then Steve does the impossible. He laughs. Giving permission to everyone in the joint. Boss and Patrick and Mary and John laugh with nervous relief. Others, strangers, farmers, barflies, laugh along, their motives harder to read. Even I laugh, in spite of myself, wanting to make the comment go away. To bring back the warm camaraderie from a moment ago.

But it is gone. Karla throws her beer at the bartender and storms out the door. I wait a moment, then, concerned, go after her.

I find her in the back of her truck, drinking a tallboy from her cooler, arms around Louise Nevelson, her rock. "Karla." I climb into the truck bed. Touch her shoulder. "Are you okay?"

She is crying. "I'm sick of this shit. I'm not a dyke. I'm not gay. Why does everyone think I'm gay?"

You're not? I don't voice the thought. I sit on the wheel well, next to a large mound of new rubber tubing.

"Mary's gay, but no one calls her a dyke," Karla says.

"Really?"

"Yeah, she's been hitting on me since she got here."

"Wow."

Louise licks Karla's cheek, the salty tears. It's quiet out

here in Springville, or Springfield, or wherever the hell we are. Karla's upending her beer, spilling it on her face, and something is making sense to me. Karla's focus on Patrick. His blue eyes and manly work ethic and blonde Viking beard. She doesn't hate him at all. Not at all. A heartbreaking impossibility. He is oblivious, will never see what I can see now, clear as resin, in her raw, inebriated face. She lights a cigarette. "I hate it here."

"Me too." The voice startles me. It's Steve, climbing into the back of the truck. "Sorry. I was lost without my hippy and dyke sidekicks."

Karla laughs. I laugh too. Steve sits next to me, on the pile of tubing. Pulls a bottle from a pocket inside his jacket. "Want some Jägermeister?"

"What the hell," I say. It is sweet and pungent, its hot assault welcome in the back of my throat. I pass the bottle to Karla, then lean against the cool steel of the truck, look up at the sky. A nearly full moon. Stars bright, like they can only be in the country. Louise settles next to Karla's feet. I feel my breath, the cool fall air, quiet, steady.

"Say," says Karla, passing the bottle back to Steve. "I'm dying to know what your formula is. For that patina."

"The ancient Korean secret?" I venture. I'm curious too.

"Ach. It's nothing," Steve says, stretching out his legs. "Promise you won't tell anyone."

"I promise." My hand over my heart.

"Me too."

"Skim milk, kosher salt, blue food coloring, and piss."

"Whose piss?" Karla pushes.

"Who do you think?"

"And you were worried about putting yourself in the work," Karla teases, accepting another drag from the bottle. I laugh quietly. The dog sighs and repositions herself. Faint music from the juke box inside the bar.

"True," Steve admits. He leans against the wall of the truck bed, his long black hair beautiful in the moonlight. A truck passes on the bumpy little highway, washing light over us, three foreign freaks and a lazy dog in the back of a rusty green pickup, banded together for safety, armed with nothing but rubber tubing. The neon Pabst sign buzzes in the roadhouse window. Next to it a feed store, closed for hours, kudzu vines creeping up the silent building, arrogant and thick, choking it to death.

The bar door opens and noise gushes out, and John Truman, dressed only in white briefs and cowboy boots, runs yelling into the empty road. Boss chases him down, grabs him roughly by the arm, drags him to his truck, throws him in. Then Patrick dashes out, arms full of John's discarded clothes, and Mary runs up to us, giggling nervously. "I think we've worn out our welcome," she says.

"Yup, time to go," Karla says, hops into the driver's seat, puts the truck in gear.

Patrick is speeding away already, Boss too, crazy John in tow, not wasting any time. "Hang on," Karla shouts through the window, as Mary slams the passenger door, and Steve and the dog and I are thrown onto the floor, a pile of limbs and teeth and rubber tubing. Something jabbing into my shoulder.

"Damn. What the hell was that?" Steve rubs a sore elbow. We're back on the open road. Good. Good riddance, Springwhatever. Back into cornfields, straight highway, aiming for home.

I sit up a little, lean against the cab. "Here." I help him to an empty spot beside me. "Louise!" The dog is hopping back and forth over the rubber tubing, making me nervous. "Sit! Sit down!" She obeys, settles between us, rests her bony chin on my knee.

"Well, I guess we're here for the long haul." Steve digs through the cooler, opens himself a beer, passes one to me. I'm already drunk, I realize, taking a pull of it. All of us are. None of us in any condition to drive, Karla especially. This might very well be the last beer I ever drink. The last ride I ever take. Steve doesn't seem nervous at all. Hangs his arm over the side of the truck. Looks straight up at the sky. "I'm glad it's not raining," he says.

A positive comment. He has a point. Rain would make this journey uncomfortable, but there is no rain, and I'm relaxing now, in spite of common sense, into my drunkenness. Karla's doing sixty, probably. My hat flies off, onto the road, and we watch it recede into darkness. "Bye," I call after it, my little felt friend. My hair is flying wild into my mouth and eyes. I lie down completely now, to get out of the wind. Steve, above me, relishes the chaos, lets his long hair do what it wants, looks up at the stars.

"I think Karla is in love with Patrick," I say. It's loud out here. She can't hear me.

"Really?" He looks down at me, just a moonlit silhouette now, his expression impossible to read. "I never thought of that. Whatever it is, she's got it bad."

"Yeah." I scratch Louise's chest as she stretches. "You know what, Steve, I'm sick of being afraid of you," I blurt.

I'm not sure why I say it. Maybe losing the felt hat has left my brain exposed and rusty, like the kitchen timer. I expect him to laugh, but he doesn't, just looks at me peripherally, back in his inscrutable mode, which I realize now is just another costume, its own kind of hazmat suit.

God, *inscrutable*? Did I really just think that? Can he hear my rusted brain thinking it, over the wheels and wind?

He doesn't say anything. He looks straight back at the road. "Hey Devo, snap out of it," I say, and reach to poke his armpit. He winces, faces me, and finally cracks a smile.

Dragster (Dragster Series), 1995
Perry Vasquez
Recycled Havoline 10w-30
on Arches print paper
22" x 30"

BELLEVILLE, ILLINOIS

christopher orlet

CARS

MY FRIENDS WERE INTO automobiles, but I didn't have a car; even if I had it would have been just a pair of wheels to me, a form of transportation to help me escape somewhere, or perhaps take me where I'd always wanted to go, hopefully with someone I loved alongside. Other guys were into drugs and booze. I was kind of into music, but I preferred to leave that to the professionals. I'd hang out with these guys and listen to them talk for hours about carburetors and transmissions and we'd listen to eight-track tapes of the awful bands they liked — Journey, Styx, Foreigner — and I'd wonder what the hell I was doing there. I would stand there for hours like a dummy, mute and bewildered, patiently waiting for my real life to start, but without the key to the ignition. Sometimes some guy I wouldn't know would ask my friends, "What's the matter with him. Don't he talk?" There were never any girls around either.

Paul

After Paul's parents divorced, he continued to live in their old house on 18th Street. There was no electricity and no water, but for Paul it was preferable to living with his new stepdad. Paul's grandfather had built the house in 1914, and now it was for sale, which was probably the reason Paul's dad came back to town one night and got loaded up on Kentucky bourbon and burnt the place to the ground. Only a few of us knew that Paul was living in the basement at the time. He came home late that night to find a large mound of smoldering ashes where his home and few belongings should have been. After the fire trucks left, I helped Paul move into his garage. There wasn't that much to move. That garage was Paul's home for nearly two years until the insurance came through and the house was rebuilt and sold to this nice young family from Arkansas.

Pipedream

Sometimes, on lazy summer afternoons, Paul and I would climb onto the roof of St. Mary's Grade School and stare out over our neighborhood drowsing in the August sun and talk about what we were going to be when we got older. This was during the big CB radio fad, and we'd decided we were going to be truck drivers — drive the big rigs and see the country. We'd be partners and take turns driving while the other slept. When the CB fad passed we forgot all about being truckers. Paul went into the Army and after that he got a job fixing flats. I took a job washing limousines. We both got married for a little while and had a couple of kids, but it is only those rooftop pipedreams that mean anything to me now.

Joby

When I was nine or ten, a black family moved into the duplex next door. This was a first for our neighborhood and I remember well how the dads on the block took it, storming around and yelling, "there goes the goddamn neighborhood." The neighborhood was never any great shakes to begin with, but it *was* fairly typical of that time and place, an odd assortment of janitors and truck drivers and salesmen and mechanics and one small business owner. This new family consisted of a woman and her two boys, a grandfather and a series of shiftless boyfriends. Sometimes my dad would get fed up waiting for the new neighbors to mow their lawn and he would push our lawnmower over into their backyard and cut their grass while the woman and her two boys stared out the dirty kitchen window in silent awe. Once I asked the younger of the two what his name was, and he told me "Joby."

"Joby?" I asked. He said, "Naaaw, Joby."

Another time the woman came home with a new baby. I asked Joby what kind of baby it was. He gave me a curious look. "A *black* one," he said.

VINNIE BARBECUE

Sometimes, after our neighbor Vinnie had had his twelfth Blatz of an evening, he would bring out his old cassette player and play Harry Belafonte songs for us. My favorite songs were "Matilda" and "Juanita," which, coming from of Vinnie's cheap cassette player, gave the neighborhood a kind of shabby Caribbean carnival atmosphere, which I guess you had to be very young or very old to appreciate. My parents were neither. They thought Vinnie was worse than useless, perhaps a bit dangerous, but I came to admire him, a lonely old jobless guy content with nothing in life but half a case of Blatz, a pair of scrawny chicken breasts smothered in green onions and Maul's barbecue sauce and the *Best of Harry Belafonte* on cassette tape. I only hope I'm half as contented as Vinnie was when I am old and broke and drunk and alone.

School's Out

My brother Frank slapped a nun once. It was right after recess. His eighth-grade teacher, Sister John Eudes, hadn't returned to the classroom yet, so Frank, goofing off as usual, took down the portrait of the Sacred Heart of Jesus and wrote "Schools Out" over the heart just like the cover of the Alice Cooper album. Before Frank could return the picture, Sister John Eudes came up and snatched the portrait. You can imagine her shock and outrage. She slapped Frank sharply across the face, and my brother, being a bit of a hothead, slapped her back. It was probably more reflex than malice, but that hardly mattered. A student slapping a nun was unprecedented. I mean, it just didn't happen. You didn't even talk back to a nun, unless it was a nun like Sister Marie Cecilia, our music teacher, who had no idea how to handle a class.

Frank was marched over to the rectory where the Monsignor was told the whole terrible story. Frank said at first he thought the Monsignor was going to have a stroke; then he feared the Monsignor was going to murder him. Frank said he thought he could have taken the Monsignor since the old man was well into his seventies, but then maybe not. He was still a tough old bastard.

My parents were called to the rectory, and somehow, after two or three hours, they talked the Monsignor out of expelling Frank. He just had to spend every recess period until graduation in the church on his knees praying for forgiveness. When they got home I was immediately sent to my room. Listening through the floor vents, I could hear my dad trying to kill Frank, and my mother pleading for him to stop. My dad kept screaming over and over, "Hit a nun, will you? Tough guy hits a nun! Come on, tough guy! Let's see you hit me!" It turned out Frank wasn't so tough after all. He crawled up the steps bawling like a baby. He told me to get the hell out of the room. I guess he didn't want me to see him that way.

Fr. Louie Louie

When we were in our early teens,we would spend a weekend each summer with Fr. Louie. The trunk of his Camaro was always well stocked with porn magazines, gin, and coolers of beer, enough to last an entire weekend on the river. Instead of saying grace, Fr. Louie would say, “Drink up, boys!” and once almost pissed his pants when our Playmate cooler momentarily washed overboard and was lost on the white rapids. Later, he would recall how, as a boy of thirteen, his mother dragged him kicking and screaming to the seminary, and how, once there, surrounded by young attractive boys like himself, he quickly got used to the idea. Particularly after he was ordained and sent to a Catholic grade school. It just kept getting better and better. If only they didn’t make you get up so goddamn early, he sighed, swirling his cocktail glass and farting in his chaise lounge under a string of cheap multi-colored lights.

Ugly Friend

In high school, I would always get stuck with the ugly friend, the fat friend, or the dull friend. My best friend Kevin, handsome and athletic, with charm to burn, got the beautiful girls, sometimes two or three. I was left with the hopeless girl, the homely girl, the suicide.

Great Bands

The black girls at work kept telling me I needed to get laid. *There* was my problem, they said. They even said they would come over Friday night and fix me up, but they were only joking. Sometimes the black girls said they envied the way white guys took responsibility for their children, even if they weren’t married to the mother. They’d tell me, “Black men will say ‘Fuck you *and* the kid.’” I said, as for white guys taking responsibility, this was happening less and less often.

Anyway, getting laid was *a* problem, but it wasn’t *the*

problem. The problem was everything that came before that. I used to go to nightclubs during the week and listen to these obscure country punk bands and there were never any girls at these shows. Girls didn't like the kind of music I listened to. But there sure were some great bands in those days.

Good Days

I started carrying around a small pocket notebook that contained a list of everything that was wrong. That way, when some idiot said, "Hey man, what's wrong?" I would just pull out my little notebook and read them everything that was on the list. Sometimes the list went on for pages and pages. Those were the good days.

A Fool's Faith

dennis dillingham

It's not your typical gravestone; in fact, it's not a stone at all. A marker, a bronze and iron plaque set into the ground, his name and the dates of his life separated by a simple, unremarkable dash, two inches of forged, stainless metal responsible for holding his sixty years. I touch it and it feels cool, cooler than the air, as if a magnet for the abounding coldness. I scratch at it, pick at it, seeing if I can release a breath of explanation, but it's well made, the metal and the color inextricably fused. I come away with nothing but a smudge of dirt on the tip of my finger and the same impossible feelings of emptiness.

A supremely natural setting: hills, trees, flowers, grass, more a park than a cemetery, which is nice, I suppose, the discretion such a place offers. From a distance, it must seem a perfectly lovely picnic spot, spreading a blanket beneath one of the looming oaks, ignoring the names and dates and dashes sprinkled throughout like dandelions. In truth, the tree my dad is buried beneath would make a great backstop for a game of Wiffle ball, wide enough to deflect all but the sharpest curves.

Games were something my dad and I always had. Unlike me, he played baseball when he was younger and was even good enough to be invited to play semi-pro for one of those rough-and-tumble, five-dollar-a-day leagues, an offer he turned down in favor of an education and a family. The experience, though, stayed with him and he understood the game, understood it better even than me, his only son, his namesake, his on-field experiences trumping whatever information I could gather from the backs of Topps' cards or listening to Mel Allen on *This Week in Baseball.* We'd talk the sport, the players, watch games together on Saturday and Sunday afternoons, lamenting blown calls, chastising poor coaching decisions, sometimes simply drifting to sleep beneath the weight of the announcers' voices.

Long-time residents of Long Island, we occasionally went to Mets' games together, a few years after that intoxicating 1986 season. Just my father and me, my four sisters and mother at home watching in hopes of catching a glimpse of us on TV. It was easier then. I wouldn't be a teenager for a few years and hadn't yet started to see my father in the way most teenagers see their parents: as liabilities in the all-consuming struggle to be independent, popular, better. The only thing I cared about was baseball. A feeling that expanded to emotionally billowing proportions on those summer nights as my father and I headed out to the Wantagh train station from our big red house on Lufberry Avenue, accompanied by a symphony of the strident cicadas indigenous to that section of suburban Long Island. With gloves and balls in tow, we boarded the Long Island Rail Road at Wantagh, switched at Jamaica, hopped the line to Woodside, switched again, and took that dirty, graffiti-ridden train out to the blue and orange oasis on the northern shore of Queens.

We always got there ludicrously early, a few hours at least, to watch batting practice and to try to get autographs. In all those years, I don't think I got a single signature. I don't know if I ever really tried. It wasn't a priority, but was really just an excuse to get there before the crowds piled in. No distractions. Just my dad and me sitting in our ticketed seats, content in our exclusive bubble of camaraderie, the green of the grass so rich it seemed almost fake, the contrast of colors the setting sun created filling our classroom- and office-dimmed eyes with rapture, all of it stirring up a stew of emotions neither of us could've described even if we wanted to. And amid all this wonder and wordless connection, the Mets trotted out from the dugout, the stadium lights igniting their uniforms to a piercing, perfect blue and white; Darryl, Keith, Mookie, HoJo, and if you were lucky, Dwight, all standing just yards away as the cool summer night chased the day's humidity, descending like a mystical, rejuvenating fog.

Those nights at Shea are some of my most poignant memories of childhood, sharing with my father something so inherently male, so inherently American and right as baseball, sitting side-by-side, sharing a bag of peanuts, a pretzel, a bladder-busting cup of soda, sharing a favorite team. In a middle-class, female-dominated, Irish-Catholic family, where emotional expression was as unlikely as missing mass on Sunday, the Mets were a meaningful source of connection for my father and me. I mean, is there anything better than being eleven years old and watching your favorite team, win or lose, with your father, the man who had always been there, the one who was immune to the laws of nature and physics, the man who would live forever?

Truth can be an elusive thing, masked in transparent yet somehow effective disguises. And what is growing up, really, but a euphemism for learning and coming to accept the sad, dangerous, and sometimes shocking truths childhood innocence keeps hidden? There are countless examples of these truths: the true identity of the Tooth Fairy and the Easter Bunny; the realization that the moon isn't made out of cheese and alligators don't live in the sewer; that thunder isn't the sound of God bowling one heck of a frame; and that even if you do get a cramp, swimming right after eating never killed anyone. Another such truth was that my father was not, after everything we had shared and experienced together, the nights and afternoons spent side-by-side cheering and jeering, a Mets fan. Never had been. It turns out that my father was—of all things—a Yankee fan. An admirer of Mantle, Maris, Yoggi, Whitey, and all the rest of the single-monichered, larger-than-life characters of his youth.

I don't know exactly how I found out, that moment of revelation escapes me. Maybe he just told me; maybe I asked him who his favorite player was when he was a kid, somehow never making the connection that the Mets didn't come into existence until 1962 and my father was born in 1942, meaning it was either root for the Yankees—the logical choice—or the lovably losing Dodgers, who few people outside of their native Brooklyn paid much attention to. All I knew was that my father took me to Mets games; we would talk about the Mets, the players, the history, the befuddling front office maneuvers, and it only followed in my mind that he was a Mets fan.

I do remember how I felt after finding out, though—not truly angry or indignant, but surprised, shell-shocked, an undercurrent of betrayal nipping at my thoughts. As long as I could remember knowing anything, I knew my father was a Mets fan. It was one of the foundations of my early belief system, a founding member, actually, along with the knowledge that hell, although warm like Florida, was no Disneyland; that Santa Claus would only come if you were sleeping; and that God punished little boys who disobeyed their parents. What was I going to learn next, that I was adopted, raised by wolves, delivered to Earth in a silver pod from a sunless planet?

My father's admission was baffling for countless other reasons. I mean, he had none of the characteristics that typically defined Yankees fans: didn't wear an ancient satin jacket or beat-up old cap that looked as if it got caught under the wheels of the 4 train one too many times; he didn't get drunk in public or call girls "babes" or guys "buddy;" he didn't wear any jewelry around his neck, gold or otherwise; and his upper lip was conspicuously absent of hair. I had been swimming with him countless times and saw no signs of cloven hooves or an arrow-shaped tail.

I was in my twenties by that time, and, although shocking, my father's admission didn't matter in any truly life-altering sense. The sport held less power over me then than it had when I was younger, the energy I once devoted to it now devoted to other, seemingly more important things: dating, making money, finding that ever-elusive contentment. Even if it had mattered more, the truth didn't take away any of the times we shared or temper any of the emotions involved. I joked with my dad about it, elbow-to-the-ribs type jabs—I told him how disappointed I was, what a paralyzing shock his confession inflicted, throwing my entire belief system into chaos and explaining that, as a Mets fan, I had an obligation to hate the Yankees and, through transference, Yankee fans. I joked that I was struggling with an irresolvable conflict of loyalty. But like most jokes, these seemingly innocent jabs hid deeper, more complicated feelings. Deep down, I knew my father had kept his true allegiances quiet because he knew how much I liked the Mets, and knew even more, in the way fathers seem to know such things, that to say something would be to damage the connection we had. As my shock dissipated, I began to feel guilty and regretful for failing to realize sooner something so fundamentally a part of the man who dedicated his life to nothing but ensuring my sisters and I had every opportunity in the world. How could I have been so blind to something that, in retrospect, seemed so obvious? How could I have been so wrapped up in myself and my likes to completely ignore his? I began to wonder what else I didn't know about him, what other truths existed that I hadn't seen due to my now apparent blinding self-obsession.

There weren't very many things my father and I had in common, outside of our physical appearance, both of us sporting larger than average heads with ludicrously large eyebrows. Some of his greatest joys came from working with his hands, fixing and building, constantly engrossed in one project or another, activities I looked at with an air of condescension, work for the sake of work, I thought. I, on the other hand, was an unapologetic product of my generation, whiling away hour after hour in front of the television, and viewing household chores and tinkering with cars as a burden, an unenviable responsibility as opposed to a privilege. Baseball was one of the few things that could instantly dissolve the distance between us, transforming us into the sort of chummy, back-patting fathers and sons I saw on those Church of Latter Day Saints commercials on Saturday mornings growing up. It wasn't over, though, I told myself, eager to somehow make amends for my twenty-plus years of obliviousness. Sure, there had been a disconnect regarding our teams, but now there was an entirely new era awaiting, one full of good-natured ribbing and rivalry, a thrilling and possibly even better chapter in our shared baseball experience. Before we got there, though, another truth boiled to the surface.

My father, forever the epitome of strength and resolve, the center of my moral, physical, and intellectual universes, was sick. He had cancer, melanoma, the penalty for all those afternoons doing nothing but sitting in the sun, warming away the manifold stresses of his life.

What did we know? We knew the cancer that had started as an ugly mole on his stomach had woven its way like the roots of a tree through his skin and into his blood stream, which meant surgeries and treatment. Time passed, a year exactly. Twelve long months of nausea and sleepless nights and biting questions about the future, during which my dad lost the energy to do the yard work and the various household projects he took such pride in. His voracious appetite disappeared. His perennially tan skin turned sallow and loose, and he seemed to be aging a year for every month he was home. I came home as often as possible during this time, which, regretfully, wasn't all that much, the 30-mile distance separating New York and my parents' house in Central New Jersey demanding too great an effort, what with all the other demands on my time such as drinking all night and sleeping all day, or wondering incessantly whether I should call the latest girl I had fallen for, whether she would call me, what I should say if she did, whether or not she saw me in the same way as I saw her. When I did come home, my dad and I would, on occasion, sit and watch the Mets on television the way we had years earlier. By then, my dad and I hadn't been to a game together in years. We moved from Long Island to Central New Jersey when I was a teenager and the trip to Shea just got to be too much. Then we got older, and the father and son trips to the stadium we had both so thoroughly enjoyed stopped. It wasn't a conscious decision on either of our parts, but just one of those victims of time and logistics. Although we had both given baseball a back seat over the years, the sport still had a power over us, and on those spring and summer afternoons and evenings when I did manage to make it home, my dad and I would again sit and watch, make comments, shake our heads and express the same astonishment at how men being paid millions of dollars a year could sometimes play so poorly. I'd make a joke, my dad would laugh. He'd tell a story about something that happened when he used to play. I would listen. Sometimes we would drift off to sleep. Like riding a bike or tossing the ball around, it came back to us, and baseball was again that easy, uncomplicated vacuum through which we could shed everything negative and worrisome occurring in our lives and simply be two men enjoying a game, simply be father and son.

We began talking about other things too during this time, the questions I had been harboring for too long sneaking out in forced, incomplete bursts, hoping to snare other truths. It wasn't easy for me, and wasn't any easier for him. Being the type of people we were — quiet, reticent, at times emotionally-distant — the truths had always been locked up and off-limits, but I tried and my dad responded as best as he could. I learned that my dad had gone to college with Rudolf Giuliani, and paid for that education himself. I learned that he had always wanted to move away from New York, and had applied to jobs in countless other cities over the years. I learned that he had sold his car to help pay for his and my mom's wedding. I learned that the collection of bottle caps on his desk was older than me. Little things, really, that started to fill in a picture of a man I realized with each new revelation I had never taken the time to get to know, a failure I was, at long last, struggling to fix.

In the end, the treatment seemed to work. The scans came back negative. Following a year out on disability, my dad's doctors gave him the go ahead to return to work, but he wouldn't be there long.

After only a few weeks back in the office, my father went in for a routine CAT scan, the let's-just-make-sure-everything's-all-right test, expecting the same clean bill of health his doctor had given him a few months before. What he got instead was the worst news he or the rest of us could have possibly imagined. The cancer that had seemed to disappear, vanishing like the Mets' bats in August, was back, this time on his liver, clinging to the fist-sized organ like algae on a stone. In a three-month span, my dad went from "cured" to dying.

"Not good, Denny," he said to me one afternoon, coming home to find him gasping for air, sitting on the edge of a patio lounge chair in the middle of the living room, the cumbersome, plastic contraption inside now as a desperate attempt to offer him comfort. The house no longer a place where we gathered as a family to joke and eat and take the naps we failed to find time for in our hectic, daily lives, but a somber, fragile ward intent on offering comfort.

The thoughts and emotions swirled. I wanted to tell him that we would do everything we could to help him fight. I wanted to hold him and have him hold me in return. I wanted—needed—him to tell me everything would be okay. I wanted to say that I was sorry for all my failures. I wanted simply to say that I loved him.

"That's okay, Dad," I said instead. "We'll get it figured out for you."

All along, I believed my dad could beat it. So did my sisters and my mother. The doctors thought so too, even despite the odds. There was just something about my father, maybe it was his size, maybe it was the confidence his calm, stoic demeanor instilled. Whatever the reason, we didn't need to be worried. He was my dad and he was going to beat this thing, all he needed was the chance. It was like facing a fastball pitcher with a corked bat, all he had to do was make contact. What was there to be worried about?

Then a week or so following a consultation with the oncologist, and a week before he was scheduled to begin another round of treatment, my dad began having trouble breathing, grew short of breath walking to the bathroom, then simply standing up.

The doctors tried everything they could, but his breathing continued to get worse, while the tumors on his liver continued to grow. After a few more days of waiting and praying, the doctors determined that it was the cancer causing his breathing problems. The disease had invaded an artery, showering my dad's lungs with countless microscopic cancer cells. What that meant, ignoring the medical caveats and purposely vague predictions, was that it was over, there was just too much cancer. The disease had thrown one by him, robbing my father of the simple chance to fight, robbing him — robbing us — of everything.

We brought my dad to the hospital on April 12th, 2003, the day after my 27th birthday, for what I thought would be the first step in his mythical recovery. On April 28th he was gone. Never has sixteen days seemed longer; never has it seemed more brief.

Not that I ever consciously thought it, but I know now that I was expecting ten or fifteen more years with my father, plenty of time to ask him all the questions I had always been too embarrassed or shy to ask before. In an instant, that decade became a matter of days, leaving all the questions I still had unasked and all the other truths still hidden.

I never expected my father to get sick; I don't know any son who does. Then when he did get sick, I never expected such a seemingly benign thing as skin cancer to beat him. And even when it seemed obvious that the disease was winning, wouldn't be deterred until it had devoured every last bit of his liver, I still couldn't keep from believing he was going to pull it out in the bottom of the ninth with a mammoth, Roy Hobbes-esque shot into the lights, showering us all with incandescent embers of joy and relief. I believed he would wake up one morning cured, the cancer fading away miraculously in his sleep like some innocuous sniffle, calmly sitting at the kitchen table diving into a bowl of Honey Nut Cheerios with bananas, his face freshly shaven and his hair combed in the vainly manicured way we all recognized, demanding we all wipe our tears and get going before the traffic got too bad. I don't regret believing that, even if it proved to be wrong, the product of the fool's faith some might have seen it as. Because that faith gave me an invaluable gift, it gave me time, a few optimistic weeks I was able to spend side-by-side with my father, wiping his forehead, helping him blow his nose, laughing and joking and pretending, despite him being bed-ridden and bound by bundles of tubes and wires, that nothing at all was wrong. Even more importantly, this ability to remain positive gave me the strength to look my dad in the eyes and tell him as tearlessly as possible exactly what he meant to me. That despite our differences, despite my emotional distance, my failures, I admired him and treasured his presence in my life. It didn't come close to making up for the opportunities to spend time with him that I let slip by over the years, didn't answer any of the questions still bouncing around my head or forgive my previous lack of interest in him and his life, but it was something and having said it helps in a way few other things seem able to.

What was this faith and where did it come from? There are the obvious answers of family and religion. But my family is not terribly optimistic and I've never, despite years of Catholic education and thousands of hours spent at church, placed much faith in religion, the institution and its tenets seeming to provide little assistance at the times when you need them most. As ridiculous as it may sound, a more feasible conclusion I've come to is baseball.

Be it by virtue of its history, its undeniable link to our national identity, its wholesome simplicity or the simple fact that it starts in spring, the season for new beginnings, baseball is a powerful catalyst for this lesson of faith and optimism, revealing so clearly the necessity and value of hopes and dreams, the existence and possibility of miracles. That's why I love baseball, loved it when I was a kid never having even played. Every year, thirty teams start the season and hundreds of thousands of fans pack stadiums, each one thinking that this year is going to be their team's year. For a few weeks, or, if you're lucky, months, anything can happen; the horizon is as bright and beautiful as you are willing to believe. And by giving ourselves up to these far-flung and desperate dreams we allow ourselves to feel, for even the most fleeting of moments, the optimism and hope that is so easily trampled in other avenues of our lives.

Who would've expected that dribbler down the first base line to scoot through Bill Buckner's legs two decades ago? Who would've expected a limping, nearly immobile Kirk Gibson to send one deep into the Los Angeles smog? More recently, who would've expected the Red Sox, of all teams, to come back from a 3-0 deficit to, of all teams, the Yankees, then go on to win the World Series in four games? No one. These things are improbable, no, impossible; they simply aren't supposed to happen. But yet, somehow, they continually do.

It may seem trite or diminishing of the immensity of things such as life and death to credit a sport, a game, with inspiring such wide-eyed and uncompromising faith. But that's just it, because for my father and me, it was never about the game, not really; never about whether the Mets won or lost—though they tended to lose far more often than win in those years—or even who was pitching or playing that night. Those facts faded from memory the moment the train pulled up to take my dad and me home. What has lasted is the memory of simply being there with my father, the feelings of rightness and of possibility that enveloped us. What has lasted is the memory of the magic I felt, the kind unique to sharing something I enjoyed and understood completely with someone I loved, someone who understood and enjoyed it too. Those feelings and that kind of connection are rare, and though we ran out of time, my father and I were fortunate to share the experience while we could.

The Ballad of Sad Ophine

lauren groff

Ophine. Oh, lord.

Ragamuffin, guttersnipe, scamp. Petite ondine of scabby knees, always perched like a bird in the oaks and aspens, slumbering like a cat in clean laundry. Ophine, belonging to nobody and everybody at once, only found where she was unexpected, which was all anyone expected of her.

Oh, Ophine, the parents would say if she were still around after dusk. Go home.

And off she would go, never taking offense — but never going home. Instead, she'd steal into the Codwalladers' kitchen after supper, helping herself to a plate of Swedish meatballs, eating with those exquisite manners of hers: pinky raised, lips closed over her yellow snaggleteeth, patting her mouth with a napkin after each bite. She'd slip through the doggy door at the Ginzbergs' and cuddle on the cedar bed with Bear, the one-legged dachshund that scootched around with a wagon under his rear. She'd climb up to the Breesee's tree house and cook herself a can of beans on the camping stove, yodeling cowboy songs through the treetops and windows, infecting the children's dreams with cacti and saddlesores.

Ohhhhhh-pheeeeeene, they'd sing along in their sleep.

And they would awaken early in the summer mornings, rubbing their eyes at the window, disbelieving what they'd see: Ophine, naked and eerie, doing underwater laps in the pools, back and forth, a skinny pale fish, blessing the morning, just so. One could never find her when she was needed, but her traces lingered everywhere — a warm depression in the cot in the maid's room; a popsicle stick on the childless Widow McCarthy's commode; a yard raked clean of leaves after a Thanksgiving trip to Florida; stealthy footsteps in the house at night, but it was only food that ever went missing. And always, always that scent of hers, that medley of pine needles and geraniums and muskrat, dirty feet and feathers and ocean. Everyone in the neighborhood loved that smell as they loved themselves; it made their hearts quicken, for they knew she was around.

Ophine was theirs, theirs, theirs, theirs, theirs, alone, for she had been left there, for the neighborhood, to share. In the late 40s, her mother had rumbled up in an Airstream Wee Wind with pompom curtains, parked by the baseball field, and thrust open the door. Little Ophine, three years old, tumbled down the steps and into their lives. Josephine, Jophine, Ophine, named after a tiny despot's goose-necked wife, of whom Ophine was a direct descendant. Is it enough to say her mother saw omens in teapot steam and made prophecies in gibberish tongues? Is it enough to say that *poof!* one day, she was gone, without Ophine? By then, Ophine was essential to the neighborhood's quotidian, that potbelly, those honest seed-pearl eyes. And although the parents continued to say, go home, Ophine, nobody thought to ask where her home was until the parents, years later, realized her mother was no longer parked by the ball field.

It was not that they didn't care, of course, but Ophine chose to tell only what they needed to know. By the time they realized she had no home, she had many, all of them, and there was no question of tying her to only one.

It suited everyone. Exactly.

Here, Ophine, the mothers would say, thrusting a bundle of their old clothes, shoes, toiletries into her arms. In every house, she had a shelf or closet or drawer, and would bedeck herself by whim; head-to-toe silk scarves one day, denim the next, contrasting reds, or in total opposite; sweaters becoming culottes, crotch-split leggings becoming a top. And they were repaid in kind, or kindness. Who do you think sat for hours on Mrs. Pea's lap, absorbing tears with the back of her head, when the years went on and the Peas failed to have a baby?

C'mere, Ophine, the fathers would say, and show her how to use the riding mower or change an oil filter or, in the case of Mr. Kanamatsu, how to transcendentally meditate in his garden filled with bells. Who do you think let Mr. Nacker read aloud his 600-page manuscript after it was rejected by publishers, and gave thoughtful, albeit juvenile, critique?

Hey, Ophine, the kids would shriek, and there she was to play first base, to judge the diving contests, to make dandelion crowns, to pull splinters from behinds when the boys tried to slide down the Morellis' porch banister. Who do you think would read their diaries, know their hatreds and their loves, and yet treat everyone the same afterwards?

And, oh, the stories to tell. There was the time the Poindexters' baby flipped himself upside down in his rubber floaty in the pool, and Mrs. Poindexter was arguing with the milkman at the door, and the little fat feet kicked slower and slower above water, when there came Ophine to grasp the baby and pull him up like an angry turnip into the good air. Or the time that Lady Hackensack (not nobility; Lady, her first name) was pinned underneath the vast portrait of her dear, departed spouse on the very weekend that Lourdes and Inigo, her helpers, were in

Xochimilco visiting family. Lady Hackensack shouted in the vast house until she lost her voice and was resigned to death by starvation, when who came after merely two hours to free her, but lovely, bony, stringy-haired, giggling Ophine.

There were bad stories, too, of course; all that happened to the children in the neighborhood happened to her, for the burden of having many homes was that she had an equal share in the many evils that happened in them. There was a belt whipping for breaking the hallway chandelier in the Browns' as she played Tarzan; there was the philosophy grad student at the Chens' who came upon Ophine as she slept in the towel closet at night, and grabbed her limp hand and rubbed it against himself until he gasped and shivered and fled. There was the time when she fell down a well and was wedged upside down, and it took the fire department four hours to rescue her. Ophine took the bad as she took the good, smiling shyly and hiding her skewed teeth with her dirty hands.

Ophine, Ophine, how you broke their hearts.

For the day came when the children of Ophine's age came home all atwitter from the last day of middle school. They laughed. They screamed. They shouted. They hit one another, they were thrilled to their cores, because they had heard the news; the Macaulay-VanDammes had bought a television set to celebrate the summer. There was high school next fall and an eternity until then, with no more boring books, no more pick-up ballgames, for now they would all be little sophisticates in the cool cave of the Macaulay-VanDammes' living room. They would munch on apples and gelatin dessert as they sat, awed, before the flashing black and white and gray.

Oh, the wonder, oh the joy.

And it was that night, that first one, the axis of it all. The streets were bare for the hour of the broadcast; no voices shouting in the sprinklers; and meals were made from cans and mixes, for the mothers wanted to watch, too. They crowded in, they gathered. Standing room only, they watched.

Nobody was outside to see Ophine sleeping forlorn in the crotch of the great elm, how her scraggly hair hung limp and her one arm dangled. Nobody saw the stranger's rumbling Cadillac, silver as a shark, come sliding through the neighborhood, slow and slowing even more. And then the clouds fell like a poncho over the roofs of the houses like so many great shoulders, and all was dark and still. Light from the television began to tremble through the window and across the Macaulay-VanDammes' vast lawn. And the Cadillac's lights turned on like eyes in the dark and pinned Ophine in the tree like a moth with wings folded up. The Cadillac purred. The car door clicked open and clicked shut. And *poof!* Ophine was gone, like that.

Because of the neighborhood's new love, because she was unanchored, because she was a little bit elfish, nobody discovered Ophine's absence until mid-July. When the slow and solemn consciousness suddenly arose in them, it was like being diagnosed with a disease after a long period of malaise.

They found that frogs had swum into the filters of the pools and rotted there, as the children hadn't been around to collect them; they realized why they all had difficulty awakening in the mornings although the grass glowed and the sunshine beckoned; they saw in the mirror that their faces were mottled in spots, pale from the darkness of indoors.

Then the whisper went around, *Ophine had run away.* The police were contacted, milk cartons printed with her picture. And then a darker whisper went around, and the bachelors' houses were surreptitiously searched when they were at work. And then the darkest whisper of all. The fathers slipped out one weekend and, pretending they were camping, combed through the forests inch by inch. No buried shoe. No ribbon from her hair.

Only then, squinting, hunched, pale, did the neighborhood children emerge into the bright sunlight, sniffing the wind for geranium, ocean, sour feet, any indication of their Ophine. They searched in the trees, they opened the closets, they kicked aside the baseball gloves, shiny and hardened with disuse. But all they discovered were their mothers at the counters, staring off into space, the fathers drinking beer in the garage, staring at the car. The children couldn't ask them where she was, for they suddenly saw their parents' sadness and didn't know how to address it. So they organized, gaining strength, pick-up tag games, bicycle trips, picnics, in the hopes of luring her back; but it was done. She was gone. Eventually, they went back inside when dusk began to fall, every day, their frozen dinners salted by the sorrow of what they'd lost.

And, over the years, they looked for her on the television, hoping to mine her face in the studio audience like a gold nugget in a stream. They looked for her in campgrounds on their family vacations. They grew hair in their armpits and gravel in their voices, and still they looked for her, in bowling alleys, at fairgrounds, trying to find her in the faces of the elastic women and bearded ladies and trapeze artists at the circus. It became a tic, their looking, and they looked and looked and looked. They went away, spilled across the country like salt from a dropped shaker. Wherever they went, they looked.

It is only now, when those children are old, that they have begun to think they see her on the sunny days of summer when they visit their grandchildren, and the television natters on in the living room, but the kids are outside, gilded by sun and rolling in the grass. Those of that old neighborhood sniff the air, catching traces of Ophine, feel the chaise lounges for warmth, find an extra lemonade glass in the sink. Once in a while, with their fading eyesight, they see a skinny body quick in a tree, but it flees before the old eyes can catch up. Do they weep, then, when they can't catch her, do they go into the broom closet and sob? They might not. Then again, maybe they might.

And what would they say, anyway, if they caught the illusion, held the skinny, giggling shoulders in their hands? Maybe they'd say nothing.

Maybe they'd say: Hello, there.

And maybe, just maybe: You were our joy, Ophine, and we are sorry. You were our joy, Ophine, and where did you go?

Interview: Salvador Plascencia

george ducker

Salvador Plascencia's first novel, The People of Paper, *is difficult to sum up in a tidy manner. The plot whirrs and cartwheels across time zones and locales, jumping forwards and backwards, from Mexican villages to El Monte, California. Real and imagined history is juggled as a wandering priest sells black market papal remedies, a drooling Baby Nostradamus predicts a dark, cubed future, and the secret origins of Rita Hayworth are finally revealed. Ultimately, Plascencia's novel centers around one of the oldest stories: Boy loses Girl, Boy strives to get Girl back. The twist is that while boy is recovering from the break-up, the boy is also writing a novel called* The People of Paper. *As the novel progresses, his characters become more and more surly and disagreeable, refusing to be led where the boy chooses to lead them, until a man named Federico de la Fe, ostensibly the hero, declares war upon Plascencia himself and his powers of omniscient narration.*

Plascencia, 29, a graduate of Syracuse University's writing program, was kind enough to take a seasonably warm afternoon this Spring to sit down and discuss such topics as his home town's inherited mythology, the comic book correlations of Ayn Rand, and the perils of putting out a first book. I made the inital mistake of putting my recorder down on the table in plain sight, and over the course of the interview, Plascencia kept putting things in front of it — salt and pepper shakers, his saucer, crumpled-up napkins; moving them as he spoke, like a man playing chess, taking and re-taking positions.

HOBART: So, you just got back from Spain. I heard a rumor that your decision had something to do with the Travel Channel late at night.

SALVADOR PLASCENCIA: I was supposed to go to Lisbon, in Portugal, but I never made it to Lisbon. It's wasn't one of those immediate *I'm gonna get away, I'm gonna go to Lisbon* kind of things. I was watching the Travel Channel and there was a thing on Lisbon, and I thought, *Okay, I'm gonna go to Lisbon.* But then I never got there. I went to London with my friend and we spent New Year's there, and then I flew to Madrid and I was going to loop around, go down to Barcelona, loop around to the South of Spain and then into Portugal, but then I got stuck in Grenada.

H: You got stuck?

SP: I had a good time. There was a British ex-pat who had this great bar there. There were people from all over — from Portugal, from Brazil. There were about two Spanish guys and everyone else was Australian, Brazilian, Chilean.

H: Were most people speaking Spanish, English, a combination of both?

SP: Mix of things. Portuguese, Spanish, English.

H: How's your Portuguese?

SP: My Portuguese is horrible. It's non-existent, actually. I was hanging out with some Brazilians and they would talk Portuguese and I would talk Spanish and there was a kind of connection. Most of the time, we could do it — it was pretty interesting. I mean, there are cognates and similarities, so you could have a pretty good conversation.

H: Did you buy anything while you were out there?

SP: What do you mean?

H: What were your purchases?

SP: Food.

H: You didn't go check out any books or museums or things like that?

SP: I went to bookstores, but I just looked because I was backpacking and couldn't really carry anything. I bought wine. I mean, it wasn't that big a deal. With globalism, you can get anything you want anywhere. I think I bought some tea.

H: With *The People of Paper,* was there an initial image? What was the very first idea that sprung in your head?

SP: The first image was a woman made of paper, and it was tied up with the actual material of the book — literally she's made out of paper, metaphorically she's made out of paper—

and what do we then do with this woman that's made out of paper? How do you touch her? What does it feel like? How does she go shopping? It started in the fairy tale vein and then it began to flesh out into more real-world implications. Like, what happens when you make love to her? She falls apart, you get cut.

H: You've started your own mythology in this book, the mythology of El Monte. A place that exists in a kind of permanent present-tense where some events happened many years previous and some events are happening right now. Were you conscious of developing this kind of permachronology? This anytime? Or was it something that formed itself gradually, as you went along?

SP: It was a little of both, but also I was really fearful of attempting an historical reality set in 1988 or 1970. Because in a way you're locked in to that possibility. If you have a time, a kind of temporal place, that's not tied to any real history, then you can jump around. You can go from Africa to the Americas back to ancient Rome anytime you want—it becomes liberating. You can put Napoleon, you can put Nixon and Kennedy on the same page. It was my own kind of weakness, that I couldn't be constrained into a small historical space and get the same mileage. I needed to jump around, cross continents and times and in that way, the mythological backgrounds helped me do that.

H: You mentioned that everything is globalized now. You bought some tea in Spain, but you could have just ordered it on the internet and had it shipped to you. Now, most of *The People of Paper* takes place in El Monte, a small town that's a satellite of Los Angeles. When you think about myths and legends coming from the same primordial soup that we all supposedly came from, everything commingling and mixing together, do you think that the El Montes of the world, and the Oxford, Mississippis of the world, the kind of small, out of the way places that people wouldn't normally go, are those more conducive to the formations of specific mythology, for myths and for fantasy, than large cities like Los Angeles or New York?

SP: Well, they're less known, right? The mythology of Los Angeles is already known and if you talk about the LA mythology people are going to recognize it immediately and say, *Oh that's from Nathanael West, that's James Ellroy,* then you recognize that mythology. But these smaller places, these satellites, haven't told their story yet, they haven't been accessed. And I'm from El Monte, we have our mythologies and nobody writes about them. A lot of it is hometown pride. I love El Monte, it's a great place so I wrote about it.

H: What kind of myths were prevalent in your family? Your mother and father and grandfather—what were some of the myths and stories that got passed down to you?

SP: Its hard to pinpoint which ones... it's more of a mode of telling stories. My uncle has these stories of crossing the border, hiding from the border patrol—being in a bush, the helicopter coming down, flying above and then flying really low, and the wind from the blades blowing away the bush so he was exposed. He tells it in such an off-handed way that it's almost funny. To him, it's just a story of crossing the border, just big machines on top of you and people chasing you. It's a kind of hyperbolic understatement. Operating in this intensified, slapstick grotesqueness of an event, and then moving on to something else. There's not any self-consciousness of how fantastical it is.

H: Sadness and romance are all tied together in your book. The first sentence of Chapter One is, *Federico de la Fe discovered a cure for remorse.* De la Fe's remorse is borne out of the failure of romance with his wife. So, I guess, broadly, if romance is the idealization of love, then isn't sadness the result of that romance, that idealization, gone wrong?

SP: Sadness is the moment where what you would feel normally is intensified. When you're sad, your whole organism starts to feel things it never felt before. Food tastes different. Sadness becomes a kind of epistemology, a way of knowing, like everything is colored though this sadness and how do you deal with it. A lot of people say that the book's very sad, and it is, but at the same time it's very playful.

H: In James Baldwin's *Another Country*, he deals with relationships from both sides; the jubilation and the heartbreak. There's a lot of both in *The People of Paper*, with Cardinal and Saturn and Froggy talking about the kind of love they had and how they lost it and how there's a possibility for them having it again, and on and on.

SP: *Another Country* stylistically is very straightforward. You think, *awww, another book about relationships in New York. Fuck.* But the book was devastating. You read it, and there's this range of emotion from extreme sadness to joy and everything in-between, and to have a book that's certainly about relationships bruise me and beat me up the way that book did, it really opened things up for me. I realized my book wasn't doing what it was supposed to be doing. Before, there were all these maneuvers, these wars, these people made out of paper. It was missing some emotional depth, and *Another Country* was exactly what the book needed. It really helped me flesh out the characters in a more emotional way as opposed to just plot movements.

H: Both books strike on the impermanence of everything, how things are mutable, changeable in regards to love and the way it affects our lives.

SP: But at the same time not, because this character, Rufus, he dies early on but he remains in the characters' minds.

They can't get rid of Rufus. He dies; he's not in the story anymore, and they're all still dealing with Rufus; they can't get rid of Rufus. Rufus stays forever even though he's dead. Baldwin may not be my favorite writer, but that's my favorite novel.

H: That's a pretty realistic book. I read somewhere that you were turned off by "realism."

SP: I don't know where you read that. I don't think you read that anywhere.
[Laughter]

H: What are you reading right now?

SP: I'm reading *Middlesex* right now. It is phenomenal. To go from *The Virgin Suicides*, which is suburban characters in a small little space to *Middlesex* which goes all over the place... I'm just excited about *Middlesex* right now.

H: He draws from a borrowed mythology.

SP: Well, the main character is telling us a story about an unlived past. It's genetic; he/she didn't really live it—it's a genetic inheritance. The story that she claims is not hers, it's only hers to tell because she's inherited it.

H: Uh. [Pause. Flipping through notebook.]

SP: Wait, where were you going with that. Realism? What?

H: Well, do you think in the future that you'll incorporate more realistic styles of storytelling? More dialogue, more of this that and the other?

SP: I just follow the sentence most of the time. I mean, that's not entirely true. But most of the time I don't know what's going to happen. I write a sentence and then I try to follow it up. What's next? What happens? Am I having fun with where things are going? If I'm not then I cut it and start over. My tendency tends to be not towards strict realism. I read Marquez, I read George Saunders, Aimee Bender, Ben Marcus, they are who I read. That's what I've always loved: Angela Carter, Rushdie, Flann O'Brien. I grew up with Dalkey Archive. It's a press that publishes Flann O'Brien and keeps all these old modernist/experimental people who go out of print, it brings them back. It brought back Ben Marcus's book. Dalkey Archive is also a Flann O'Brien novel. I grew up with them, so it's like: that's who my uncle is.

H: What were you reading in high school or middle school?

SP: In high school. It's shameful. The gateway writers, I guess.

H: Who are the gateway writers?

SP: Shameful. Ayn Rand, I mean, also Oscar Wilde, also J.D. Salinger. But it seems like you start reading, at least in my high school experience, you either read Oscar Wilde or you read Ayn Rand. If you were reading, that's what you were reading.

H: Were your friends reading Ayn Rand?

SP: My friends weren't doing much reading back then.

H: But how did this duality work out? Were there reading factions?

SP: It was a duality, but I was really into both of them. Oscar Wilde was aesthetic, really witty, very ambiguous moralistically, politically. Ayn Rand had these ugly sentences and this dogmatic philosophy, wasn't very aesthetic at all. At the same time, you could follow the story, you knew who was good, who was bad. In a way, what I wanted was a synthesis of Oscar Wilde and Ayn Rand. I wanted them to come together somehow, but they never did.

H: What was your favorite Ayn Rand book?

SP: I don't want to talk about it.

H: The only one I read was *The Fountainhead*

SP: [Long Pause] Well, there's a scene in *Atlas Shrugged* where these philosophical archetypes become superheroes, kicking down doors, and it becomes like a Marvel comic.

H: So you've got *Reason* trying to beat up...

SP: I forget what it was, but there were definitely *Ideals* at war with each other. More like *X-Men* than anything else. Like Magneto versus Professor X.

H: Clearly defined moral characters?

SP: But *X-Men* is way more ambiguous than Ayn Rand. Even Magneto is torn between fighting the X-Men, but at the same time he's fighting the humans.

H: Well, he is a mutant. He's conflicted.

SP: He's standing up for the mutants. At the expense of the humans. There's a little bit of eugenics in there.

[Long digression about different serials of *X-Men* comics]

SP: I was never into D.C. I was a big Marvel guy.

H: D.C. was more of the school of thought that: this guy's a super hero, but only because he has a special belt. And with Marvel, the characters were kind of *stuck*.

SP: What about Iron Man? He was all technology and research and he had the money to do it, right?

H: He had the suit. He paid for the suit.

SP: Batman was a very bourgeois superhero. He could afford it. Same with Iron Man.

H: With the X-Men, their powers were inherent, there wasn't anything they could do about it.

SP: It was a curse.

H: What's a writing day like for you?

SP: I have fevers. I won't write for two months and then I'll have a fever and I won't talk to anybody for three, four days. Unless I have a deadline and then I'll set up three hours today, four hours tomorrow. Usually, I'll just use the fever up for four days or however long it is, and then I'll stop.

H: Recouping?

SP: Sometimes it starts with the fever and then you have a trajectory and you hammer it out and then I just kind of think about it and not do anything for another two weeks, three weeks.

H: Do you listen to music?

SP: If it's a new album, I can't do it. If I know the album, it's fine.

H: What kind of music were you listening to while you were working on *The People of Paper*?

SP: It was the radio, it was everything. It was always *A Love Supreme*—John Coltrane, and The Smiths. Somehow they're always around. I grew up with The Smiths. Everything except *Strangeways*. I mean, *Louder Than Bombs* isn't really an album, but *The Queen is Dead* was my first Smiths album. I had a tape and I remember taking it home and I was like, who are these people? I was a freshman in high school and I played that tape until it busted.

[Long digression about bootlegs]

H: Going back to the actual creation of the book...

SP: Back to talking about the book? Not bootlegs?

H: Is there a moment that sticks out in your head the most about actually writing the book? I hesitate to use the word 'favorite,' but what is the moment that jumps out at you first when you think about the act of sitting down and working on the book?

SP: There was a Chris Mazza story called "Is This Sexual Harassment Yet?" and it's written in columns with a dueling narrative between the male and the female so these two columns are always battling back and forth, and I really liked that dynamic, of these two columns talking to each other. I read that story and I thought, *Why don't more people do this*? So I tried it. I kept trying it and kept trying it and it wasn't working, and suddenly (what ends up being Chapter One in the novel) I had this kind of third person voice. This little girl and a Mexican wrestler in two different columns, and I put them together and it worked. I thought that I could have these simultaneous, complimentary voices all on one page and that was the moment where I got really excited and thought, *I can write a whole novel this way*. That was the initial plan, but that wasn't sustainable either. So you have these nice stops. You have a three column chapter, then you take a break and go back to more traditional formatting.

H: The question is, so you've written the book in Syracuse...

SP: I didn't finish it in Syracuse. I'd written two-thirds of it, then I came back to LA and spent a year and a half more. Then I sent it out, then I got an agent, the agent sent it out, it got rejected universally, and then McSweeney's called up. They published an except of it before that, and then a year later, they said hey, let's do the whole book. Eli [Horowitz] made that book work. Before, its shape was there, but a lot of the connects were missing, and Eli would say, *We need that person again, we need to link this up, this person should be happier or sadder or why is this person missing or why is this person here?* And it wasn't about cutting things out viciously, it was more about justifying characters and situations and elaborating.

H: When did layout come into play?

SP: I handed the manuscript to them basically how it looked when it was published, only the pages I gave them were regular 8½ x 11. We had to fill some pages in because of the format of the book. There would be some gaps, like six inches at the end of a column that I might have to fill up or take out. During the war, Eli would suggest small fill-ins for whenever there were gaps in the actual pages of type. Eli did the layout and it took him a day, maybe two days, and it wasn't an issue.

H: They say, what is it? "Good writers borrow, great writers steal?"

SP: It's an Oscar Wilde quote: "Talent borrows, genius steals."

H: What is something that you stole blatantly outright during the process of writing your book? It could either be in your book or something you used to actually write it, anything.

SP: The format is Chris Mazza from "Is This Sexual Harassment Yet?" So that's pretty blatant. Also, I would read Vonnegut and he had those pictures that he drew and to me it was so liberating and exciting it made me want to do what he did in terms of pictures in a book. But also, having read Marquez, I thought about how I could make it about that too, so in a way the book became this compilation of all these writers I love.

H: What is something you indulge in compulsively, to the extent that it causes you some degree of guilt?

SP: Sports. I can play soccer all day or watch basketball all day. My first love was basketball.

H: Do you watch soccer at all?

SP: With soccer, there's like eighty leagues: Premier, Mexican League. Where do you start? I just jump around.

H: Has anyone in your family read the book yet?

SP: My parents can't read English, so that's nice. I definitely tried to have it both ways with this book, mixing the memoir with the fiction, and everyone wants to know what's true and what's made up, and my parents would probably know what's true.

H: They would immediately hone in on the reality and base their opinions on that?

SP: The book is pretty intimate. And I don't want my parents to be that intimate.

H: With all the James Frey and JT Leroy...

SP: I never read Frey, but now that I know it's fiction, I want to read it. Before, I didn't care. I didn't care about memoir. As Frey just proved, memoir is limiting, reality is limiting, why would you want to stick to it? But now that I know it's fiction, I want to pick it up. I'm much more concerned about the story than the reality behind the story. JT Leroy is a performance; it's this beautiful thing, who cares if it's not real? I never had this investment in the reality of these books, the real-world correspondence; I'm interested in the story. Every film, every novel, it's all a hoax, it's about how can I trick you into my world. And now, as it comes out that Frey's book isn't real, my response is, who the fuck cares? If the story has great sentences, who cares if it's fake, real, imaginary, or lived? It's not like they're lobbying for war or some kind of political position. It's about the reading experience. Being a trickster. Can I seduce you into my world?

H: Have you talked to Liz lately?

SP: I talk to everybody in that book because we're all friends.

H: Any responses?

SP: She won't read it, but whatever.

H: She won't read it?

SP: She refuses to read it. We're friends, we're amicable. It's not... you gotta look at the novel as a time capsule. It's not this intensified feeling forever. Also, the book is not real. Except when it is. The reality and the made-up and the fantasy—what's the better narrative? That's what matters.

H: Tell me your future.

SP: I don't know the future, George.

H: Do you want to stay in Whittier? Are the mountains really blue?

SP: The San Gabriels are totally blue. We play soccer out there every Saturday. It's beautiful. There's a nice stand where they sell everything from burritos to oranges with salt. We're the *Chupacabras*, the goat-suckers. We had a tough match last Saturday against the number one team in the league. We tied two-two. Bu the game before that, we got shot up eleven-zero.

H: What do you play?

SP: Fullback. We're not very organized. We had the same personnel against a weaker team and we lost eleven-zero, then all we do is get a better formation and we tie with a supposedly great team. It's all about the formation, even in sports.

H: Columns and lines.

SP: Columns and lines and filling the lanes.

I FIND HIM SWEATING under a burned out streetlight on the Brooklyn Bridge, one cigarette hanging from his lips and one shaking in his hand. “It’s whiskey,” he says. “I’m going to sweat out the whiskey. I sweat whiskey, shit beer. Wine gets cried out. Rum gets fucked out. But this is whiskey.

“I left her. So what? Do I know you? I think maybe I do but how could I?”

“I know your face,” I say. It’s starved and shivering and moist and young. His face is a thunderstorm. “Can I get you anything?”

“Oxygen.”

“Do you want to come home?”

“Please.”

I take the cigarette from his hand; he collects papers and sneakers.

“Do you know what the first thing I remember is?” he says. “The first thing I remember is the glow of my mother’s cigarette moving in the dark as she sits on the floor watching me through the bars of the crib."

I wake in the middle of the night and he's there, sitting on the windowsill stringing cigarette butts into a crown as if they were daisies. In the morning when I go to brush my teeth, he is scrubbing the toilet. I have a zit in the middle of my cheek and he stands to pop it for me. He watches from the bed while I dress, pulls me onto his lap so he can hook my bra. I hear his breath behind me on the stairs, and when I get to the door he is already there, holding it open. When I walk down the street he goes ahead of me, sweeping the sidewalk. He pays my bus fare and then steps back down the stairs; he stands under the glass watching the bus leave. From the window at work I see him down across the street, sitting outside Rite Aid—his chin propped in one hand, scratching his head with the other. Sometimes he is smoking, sometimes reading. Sometimes he is playing the harmonica. Sometimes, but not often, he line dances. Sometimes he plays jacks. Sometimes he is drawing with chalk on the sidewalk. Sometimes he feeds stray kittens, darns socks, whittles, gives massages, plays cat's cradle, attempts to give himself the Heimlich, cries, spins, pretends to get shot, lies perfectly still on the sidewalk staring up at the sky. When I get home he is inside me and it is bliss—furious, famished bliss.

"There are some things you can't hide," he says.

"Like what?"

"Like leprosy. Leopards are hard too, in the city. Lobsters you can hide in a pot but the smell soon gives them away."

We are in bed for days, flickering in and out of sex like fireflies. He huddles his head between my legs and kisses me as if I could kiss back down there. We are sore all over.

"I'm going to lock you in a little metal box," he says.

"You'll have to catch me first."

I roll off the bed and run around the apartment, leaping over the coffee table, grapevining up and down the hallway, skipping over the couch.

He shakes his head. "I can't."

I run back to him, stand just far enough away that he can't reach me. "You're out of luck then."

My heart is smiling and I laugh. I feel joy like a tumbling building—debris crashing and burying me so I can't breathe—joy rushing into me like a cloud of soot. Joy that scares me half to death.

He is burrowed behind the washing machine dry heaving over mismatched wool socks.

"I am so weak," he stammers—eyes trying to push out tears, throat trying to push out bile, fingers wedged between his toes—"I can't feel them. They're stumps and the washer is grinding into my hipbone but who cares?"

He laughs like a ship burning. I light another cigarette and throw the old butt into the suds.

I let my torso fall over the machine; my head and arms hang behind it. He is trembling. I want to steady him, and I could, my hands are close enough to the curve of his back. But I'm afraid if I do he'll stay there, soldered to me, and we'll shake with the bulk of the washing machine between us forever.

When the cigarette is done I pull him out, and he slumps against the wall. I crouch over him and wait for him to look up. He doesn't, so I take off my shirt and lift his hand to my breast. He opens his eyes and raises his head. He laughs again.

"Nice try," he says.

He is lying behind the television. I sit down and hold his feet in my lap. They are calloused and dirty, and I press them to my stomach. He curls his toes and I feel the untrimmed nails dig into my stomach a little. I lean down and kiss the veins going into his ankles. He takes one foot and reaches it under my slip.

"Do you think we ought to get married?" he says.

I laugh. I cradle his ankle with both hands as he wiggles a toe just barely inside me.

"You're all I've ever wanted," he says. "Are you happy? I am. Don't leave me. Please, say you never will."

I start to braid some of his ankle hairs. I feel his moist toe sliding up. I want to fuck his foot. I don't want to promise.

I tell him I'm happy. I am. I'm elated.

I come home, and he is waiting on the stoop.

"I'm pregnant," he says. "Can we keep it?" His eyes lift from his belly. He takes my hand and puts it under his shirt. "It's not kicking but I think you can hear its heart beating, unless that's my blood. Feel it anyway."

The sky is purple and about to collapse. His skin pulses quickly and gently under my fingertips, and I look at his hopeful eyes.

"Hush little baby, don't say a word," I sing. "Momma's gonna buy you a kiwi bird."

He is pulling the hairs from my scalp, one by one, stretching them out in front of the sunlight and then putting them in his mouth and sucking.

"Do you think," he asks, "if I swallow them, baby will feel them? I want him to feel your hair. I want him to taste it."

Cold rushes to my edges. A pigeon walks in the window and over the couch onto my foot. It circles, its cold claws wet and dirty on my skin. One of its toes is lost and it pecks at the place where it should be, looking at me with its awful oily eyes. I look away and it flies out the window and over the street.

"I think maybe he feels it," he says. "He feels like he's happy."

The structure of birds is so precarious. They barely exist; you could crush them with one hand.

"You're right," I say. "I think he does."

Now he is cowering under the couch, building a cradle out of toothpicks.

"What's the use?" he mumbles. "It's not going to make it. I'm going to find its shredded bloody tissues in the toilet one day with my piss. And then it's going to cry to me with its awful voice I've always known echoing in the porcelain: Put me to bed. Tuck me in. Will you read me *The Giving Tree*? Can Mommy come sing to me just one more time?"

He looks up and sees me. He smirks and peels glue off his fingers.

"You're going to leave us aren't you," he says. "You're going to leave us and then it's going to be bye, bye baby."

"You don't know."

"I don't know that you'll leave, or that when you do baby will disentangle and the feathery bones and just forming veins will come collapsing out of me like waste, and I'll be all alone with the torn fetus and this stupid fucking gluey mess of a cradle? Which one? It doesn't matter. What's the use? Don't kid yourself, dear."

He has bitten my fingers down so much that they are all blood and holes. He has peeled my nails mostly off with his teeth. I can't touch anything without it digging into raw flesh. When they grow back they will be rough and strained and then I don't know who I'll be.

Today he is smiling, bouncing back and forth in the rocking chair quilting and thinking of names.

"Aloysius, Babe, Cal, Desmond, Ezekiel, Fred, George, Herbert, Indiana, Joe, Kirkpatrick, Leo, Mister, Ned, Orson, Peter, Quill, Rupert, Sam, Theodore, Ulrich, Val, Willy, X, Yogi, Zechariah.

"Today he kicked," he says, "for sure. He kicked and I think he had gas. You don't have anyone you'd like to name the child after, do you?"

"I'd like to name it Cleopatra."

"He's a boy, dear."

"How about Cleopat?"

"I'll consider it. He is mine, really, so I of course have the last word. I've been thinking about Baron.

"How was work? Do you have a headache? Put your feet up. Dinner will be ready at 6:30. Shall I get you the newspaper? A cocktail? Your pipe?

"So, I'm fairly certain he had gas so I'll have to pay better attention to what I'm eating. You know there must be something inherently superior about organic food but I'm sure I don't have a clue as to what it is but I ought to buy it anyway."

The rain comes down like it's judgment day, and the wind pours in and cradles our backs. We're eating hot dogs in front of the fireplace—hot dogs and root beer.

"There's something awful about you," he says. "You don't seem to care if baby lives."

There's lightning sharp and brutal all around. I throw the hot dog into the flames and crawl out the window onto the fire escape. I'm drenched straight through instantly, and my hair flattens against my face and shoulders. I close my eyes and thunder cracks through my body.

"I'm sorry," he's saying through the window. "I'm so sorry. Please. Come back. I'm sorry."

I am so hungry for him I salivate. I get sick with hunger. My whole body starves. When he is with me there is burning glee, but still the hunger and the cold. His belly gets bigger and we gather around it to listen to baby gurgle, and to feel its lungs going in and out, and its limbs forming. I put my chest against his stomach and my head on his heart, and I feel all three hearts beating, and I wrap my arms tight around him and fall asleep.

He has taken all the hair from my head and now he is working on my eyebrows. He tugs them out while I am sleeping and I wake with holes in them. He is swallowing the hairs,

I'm sure. There is no trace of them anywhere. I look between the sheets and in his socks and under the stove. Nothing.

He walks through the door and sits against the refrigerator cross-legged, staring at the leg of his pants.

"I brought home a yellow-jacket. I found her lying on my pants, looking like she was trying to suck something out of them. I stared at her for a while and she stopped moving and I wondered if she was dead. I flicked at her with a pen, and she started to rub her head and then walked around a little. Then she rested again and brought a leg up to her backside. I saw the big hole there, no stinger, nothing, but she was trying to scratch it, and I felt so sad for her I brought her home."

I sit next to him against the linoleum and press my hand to baby. I feel the mass of hair snarling around in his belly through the shirt.

"It's going to drown," I say. "You're going to tie baby in knots."

"You don't know what you're talking about. I'm just putting hair on his chest."

I feel weak. I feel tired. Sometimes it is difficult even to raise my eyelids. My body is a landscape of jutting precipices and skin sagging around taut hollows. He is soft and plump. His chest even seems to have grown full in anticipation. The joy I feel when he holds me takes all my energy and makes even my bones ache.

I try to stay awake to guard my skin, my teeth, my blood, my insides. I have caught him with a speculum trying to scrape away at my cervix. The hair doesn't bother me anymore, but now he brings a washcloth to bed to soak up the sweat that pours out of me while we are fucking. He wrings it into his mouth when we are done, and then he folds it over the bulge, tucking baby in.

"Sleep well, son," he says. "Please sleep. Sleep while your brain is still just a muddle, while you can sleep without dreaming of soot, and your screams buried under flaming concrete, and your mother a torn apart face running into the dark, running away."

"You know I can't run anymore," I say.

The skin there begins to pull and stretch, and we walk down the street looking into the wide eyes of babies. He turns his head to watch them pass.

"If only he could ever look like that," he says, "even that last ugly one; that child was an imp—even if his skin was bubbly with acid, even if he had a shrunken head, even if he had tongues for arms and no dick, even if he died as soon as I saw him. I don't think I'll be able to make another."

The scalpel presses into my shoulder and I am jerked awake, frozen. I hear his breath hovering above me, and I say, "Please." He doesn't answer but breathes heavily against my breast. It pierces my skin and I look away, sobbing, the cold around me tight like saran wrap.

He says, "I love you," positioning the vial beside my arm to collect the blood and the wasted skin.

I pull away and huddle against the wall.

"Go sit in the corner," I say. "Go put on the dunce cap. Go jump off the fire escape. Go shove a fucking coat hanger in there for all I care."

He slinks away from me, his neck bent like a safety pin. He moves down off the bed and into the corner, scratching at his belly and muttering, "Oh, my dear, my dearest dear," over and over again.

"We only wanted a little," he says at last. "We're thirsty and weak."

The blood is warm; it falls slowly, branching down over my chest and into my armpit. He has dropped the vial, and it lies empty on the floor. I go to him, hold out my shoulder.

"Take it," I say. "Don't waste it."

His mouth is soft and gentle and grateful. He sucks like an infant hushed in the night by his mother's tit. When the bleeding has steadied he laps at the stain that runs down my chest with his rough tongue. I never feel teeth, just moisture and suction and tears.

"I'll get all of it," he says, "if it takes a week. I'll get it. Don't worry."

I wake without breath. All motion in my body seems to have stopped. I put my pinky in his nostril and he wakes with a start.

"What? What is it?"

I open my mouth and bring his hand to feel the stillness in my lungs. I point out the window.

"All right," he says. "I'll take you."

We take the subway to Coney Island. I sleep in his lap on the way out and he whispers in my ear that the people in the car are looking at us like we are incestuous teenagers running away from home. When I lift my head we are above ground, and I turn, peering out the window like a toddler trying to see through the softening darkness. I make out clotheslines and empty lots, a naked man waiting for dawn on his roof, dark smoking youths playing soccer with a Coke bottle down in the empty street, trees and boarded up windows.

"Are you breathing?" he asks.

I shake my head.

When we get into the open air he walks me past the caged freak show and bumper cars and hot dog stands, past men strewn across the sidewalk like rubbish, the abandoned roller coaster before us on the horizon—weeds choking it like boa constrictors. Above the boardwalk the gulls circle, screeching at the first glimpses of light, predatory and large to the point of deformity. Men cast their fishing lines from the pier.

We climb over the railing and onto the sand. He ties our shoelaces together and slings the shoes over his shoulder. I tell him to be careful of glass; he says it doesn't matter.

"I could fall into a shark's mouth and not feel it," he says.

“I wish you wouldn’t go.”

The sand is cool and wet on our feet as they sink in. We walk through the plastic rings of six-packs, bottles, plastic bags, paper dishes splattered with ketchup, dirty magazines, umbrellas stretched inside-out, votive candles, popcorn, prize stuffed-animals forced to fight with strays and left for the birds to pick at. We sit enlaced—he leans against my chest and I wrap my legs around his belly—at the edge of the wavering skirt of the ocean. I can feel baby’s breath against my calves in deep, even pushes as steady as the waves. Sitting inside each other, feeling the sun begin to push through the project towers in the east, we all breathe deep and fill our bellies with hope for each other. We are warm and fat and bubbling with it.

Wedding Factory

douglas light

Charlie's at the wrong wedding reception. It's taken him nearly half an hour to realize that everyone's Indian, or Afghani, or Argentinean, from some place he's never been, someplace he'd be hard pressed to locate on a map. The thought slightly sobers him. So does the fact that everyone's shouting at him, holding their heads in their hands. He doesn't understand a word they're yelling, the language foreign and pitched.

It's Saturday, near noon, and already the day is terribly humid. The month of June, a time for weddings and arguments.

The music, the dancing, has stopped. An old woman, her skin as brown and wrinkled as a baked apple, lies on the floor, the hem of her cream-colored dress scorched. The air reeks of burnt fabric and hairspray.

The cigarette still smolders in Charlie's hand.

"This is all a mistake," Charlie says, apologizing to the woman, to her husband, to the crowd. He's a Hoosier, from

Indiana, has been in New York a year and a half and still hasn't been to the top of the Empire State Building.

"This is you!" the husband says, pointing at Charlie. "It is you, the burner of my wife! Get him!"

Charlie finds he's waving a full bottle of wine like a club or a frozen leg of lamb. "I will. Believe me, I will," he says, not certain what he's threatening. He makes for an exit, the nearest door out. Voices chase after him, but no one follows.

The Carmine Palace, on the outskirts of Babylon, Long Island, is a sprawling wedding factory. It's able to hold seven parties at once, turn out as many as twenty-one gatherings a day. Souvenir T-shirts are sold alongside cigars and discretely displayed condoms at the concierge's desk. The restrooms often run out of toilet paper.

Charlie's here for a reason.

Pushing through a fire exit onto a browning patch of lawn, Charlie's confronted by an overzealous peacock. "Sweet baby Judas," he says, startled by the bird. He's never witnessed a peacock up close, and doesn't understand why there's one here. It fans its plume, bright and brilliant and beautiful, struts a tight circle around him as it cries out.

He tries to gently shoo the bird away. "Scat, go," he says, but the bird moves closer, brushing Charlie's pant leg with its arching feathers. Charlie drops the bottle of wine, snaps his fingers, then claps his hands. "Fuck off," he says, terrified by the bird, its closeness, terrified by how the day is rapidly turning on him. The bird raises it wings and, screeching like a car wreck, rages at Charlie, attacking his legs with its beak and talons. "Goddamn," Charlie says, fighting the bird off with feeble swipes as it pecks and tears at his pants. Finally, a well-placed kick sends the bird into retreat. It cuts across the grounds, not looking back, its tail folded and its small feet peddling.

Charlie, shaken, brushes off his pants, examines his scratched hands. His shirt, damp with sweat, clings to his chest and stomach. It's too hot to wear a wool suit, but he's wearing one. It's his only suit. "What was that?" he asks himself, confused and frightened. "What just happened?" He's worried the attack is a harbinger, that bad fortune is setting in.

A row of dying hedges divides the Carmine Palace grounds from the busy roadway. A Taco Bell, a T.J. Maxx, and a Texaco fill the asphalt lot across the way. It's the suburbs, with its malls and drive-thrus, all the reasons Charlie left Indiana. He'd come on his own to New York, fought to stay afloat since moving to the city; he budgeted his money, did his laundry in the bathtub, procured toilet paper from cafés, left the lights in his studio off, and ate ramen, pasta, potatoes, foods cheap and filling. He'd held tight, survived.

Picking up the bottle of wine, he tries the door he exited. It's locked. Car exhaust from the busy road crowds the air.

Charlie rounds the building's corner, looking for an entrance, a way back in, and comes upon a tented area, another reception. Strolling through the crowd, he looks for people he knows, for the open bar, looks to see if this is Renee's reception.

A rowboat tilted on its side is filled with iced oysters and shrimp. The crowd is made up of men who talk on phones for a living and women who take water exercise classes. "Have you seen that thing, that bird?" Charlie asks a young woman standing next to the boat. She's plucked and pretty in a way that doesn't hold up well under bright light. Charlie imagines seeing her in a nightclub or at a party in a shag-carpeted basement and falling hopelessly in love with her.

Now, in the open sun of the day, she looks faded and hung-over, in desperate need of a nap.

He takes a corkscrew from the bar and uncorks his wine bottle, pours her a glass without her asking. "A beast," he says. His hands tremble. He holds one out to show the wounds. "Nearly took my eyes out," he says. "I should call PETA or the Audubon Society or whoever and have them come put that thing down. It's dangerous."

Her name is Simone. It's her birthday. She's nineteen, lives with her parents. She says, "My mother walks in on me in the bathroom this morning and says that only once in her life, for one single day, will she be exactly twice my age. Today's that day, she tells me. I was standing there naked and my mother tells me this. What am I suppose to think? I mean, really, what is she saying?"

"Is she here?" Charlie asks, loading up on shrimp. He started drinking far too early, or rather, hasn't stopped drinking from the night before. He's amazed he made it here at all, impressed himself by dressing in a suit and tie and finding the right train from Penn Station to Babylon.

He's here for a reason.

"She's the bride," Simone says, motioning toward a woman in a long, silver dress. Simone's fingers are red and blotchy, like she's bitten them or got them caught in a closing door. "It's her third wedding."

"Wow," Charlie says, feeling his energy drag. He thinks of Renee, of how, back home in Krotchersville, Indiana, they'd been a couple, had lived together.

"Three times," Charlie says to Simone. "That's, well... what happened to the first two husbands?"

"Nothing," she answers. "Or everything. I mean, that's him," she says, pointing across the crowd to the redheaded groom, who is wearing a tuxedo and bolo tie. He has a thick mustache that reminds Charlie of a wedge of dry orange. Simone takes a deep drink of wine, nearly emptying her glass. "Glen. He's the first two. This is their third try."

Glen snaps around, like he has a preternatural sense of hearing. He glares at Charlie.

Charlie looks away. "You like this Glen guy?" he asks Simone.

"Kinda have to," Simone answers. "He's my father." She holds out her glass for refill.

Charlie refills it.

"The guy is way overprotective, though. It's like he has to know what I'm doing every minute of the day. I mean, I go to the movies, and there he is, two rows behind me. I visit the gynecologist and he's sitting in the waiting room, reading

Good Housekeeping," Simone says. "It'd be kinda sweet if it wasn't so creepy. But listen," she says, unexpectedly pressing close. "This place is a bore. Everyone here works for Glen or is in my mom's book club. So, I was thinking, if you're up for it..." She pulls a small baggie from her purse, holds it out for him to see. It holds a tablet. "Ecstasy," she says.

They split it, placing it under their tongues.

Within twenty minutes, the afternoon turns supernova.

Together, they roam the different receptions, dance in a Greek line dance, match rounds of Kettle One vodka with an unemployed dentist with crooked teeth, clap after a terse toast from the father of a bride about the importance of commitment and mutual funds, and force down a plate of overcooked salmon with a side of undercooked rice at a gathering where the Cuban groom's family is visibly upset by the fact he married a Puerto Rican. Hours, days, years pass. Charlie sees the beauty in everything, in saltshakers, the cracks in the wall, the choking odor of Chaps cologne.

He finds himself in a women's room stall with Simone, sweating out the last radiant glow of the ecstasy. His scalp feels like it is being pulled from his skull. Simone leans against him, places her head to his chest. Charlie's never felt so much love, not even with Renee. He's in love with all, even the unlovable, and resolves to get his life in order. The wedding reception, the reason he'd come, is forgotten. He's going to ask Simone to marry him, ask her to run away with him. Maybe back to Indiana.

Someone bangs on the stall. "Get out!" Glen, Simone's father, demands. "Don't make me count to three!" he says. "Goddamn it, don't make me count."

"Jesus, Glen," Simone says, calmly opening the stall. "Are you supposed be frightening? Really, you can't play the hard-ass with a moustache like that."

Glen disregards his daughter, glowers at Charlie. "I'm pretty open-minded," he tells Charlie. "But you. This. Here. In the women's toilet. With my baby girl." Turning to a sink, Glen scrubs his hands with hot water and soap like he's just handled something dead. "It's a pork roast in the synagogue," he shouts. "See my daughter again and I'll—"

"Glen," Simone says, "I can do—"

"I see you with her again—" He breaks off, stares at Charlie in a mirror. "I see you," he says, then licks the tips his moustache with his tongue, fixes his hair by motioning at it. "I see you."

"My God, Glen, you're embarrassing me," Simone says. "Come on," she says, and leads Glen out of the restroom. "Bye," she calls to Charlie as the restroom door closes.

The last good feeling is flushed from Charlie. He's come for a reason and now is jittery, on the point of crying.

This is all a mistake, he thinks, drinking a half-gallon of orange juice to level out his emotions. He searches his pockets but can't find his cigarettes, can't find his keys or wallet. Can't find anything. He's lost everything.

The day builds. He listlessly moves about the Carmine Palace like a boat in a churning wake, shifting from one party to the next. Finally, he comes upon Renee and her party, then realizes it's not Renee or her party. Each gathering, each couple is the same. Everything's the same, the setups, the food, everything. Tuxedos rented. Bridal dresses paid too much for. A package deal picked from a laminated card. There's nothing special about any of them, nothing distinguishes one reception from another. It's an assembly line, a continuous event with people being replaced every few hours, one newly married couple rotating in for another.

Standing in the hall that's built to look like a replica of a Roman temple, Charlie's hard pressed to state what his purpose is. He's here for a reason, though it no longer makes sense.

After they'd dated a month, Charlie and Renee moved in together, split the rent on a one bedroom that overlooked a dormant set of train tracks, and settled into a clear, pleasant pattern. Charlie worked at the Krotchersville Coffin Factory, a job whose monotony was slowly killing him, while

Renee waited tables at the Spartan Bar and Lounge. After a year, he gave her a ring, asked her to marry him, asked her to move to New York. He'd saved, had money to move, to marry. He'd dreamt of New York all his life, what it offered, what he envisioned he'd gain. The city, he was certain, held all the answers. "We need to do more," he told her. "This, here, Indiana, we're dying."

Renee turned from him, picked up a dishrag and wiped her hands, even though her hands were dry and clean. She was unable to look at him. "Charlie," she said, then said no to both, the marriage and New York. She looked at him. "This is all too much," she told him, her eyes glimmering and moist like she was on the verge of crying. She wasn't. "I'm not certain about all this," she told him, her voice calm. "Listen, your idea, us together forever," she said, rubbing her hands with the thin towel. "No."

Charlie finds himself helping the Carmine staff set tables for a five-hundred person reception. "My God," he says to the obese man working next to him, "who knows this many people? Who has this many people in their life?"

"No one," the man says, sweating profusely. He wipes his face with a cloth napkin then refolds it, sets it on a plate. "No one knows this many people. They open a phone book, call friends of friends of friends. It's all for show. It's all to say 'Look at me and how much I'm loved.' Pure bullshit."

Charlie smokes a joint with him out back by the Dumpster. "What's the story with the peacock?" Charlie asks. "The thing nearly killed me."

"The *what*?" the man asks, concentrating on the joint. "The peacock? Is that like your code name or something? Are you undercover? 'Agent Peacock,'" the man says, coughing violently as he laughs. "'Agent Peacock, stand down. That's an order!'"

"I don't know what I'm doing," Charlie confides, feeling a need to talk. "I'm here and I'm talking to you. I'm in Long Island and I know no one." He has an urge to explain his loneliness, his uncertainty, the fact that the world seems to be closing in on him. "I'm here," he tells the man, "and I'm lost. What's happening right now? I mean, what's everyone doing?"

"A lot of them are eating," the man says, pulling heavily on the joint. He holds the smoke deep in his lungs, his face turning red. "Even more are drinking," he says, letting out his breath, a sour cloud. "Shit, have you seen this?" he asks, taking Charlie by the arm. "I got to show you this. It'll break your heart." He guides Charlie through a back door of the building, down a set of stairs into the basement and along a dark hall. "Here," he tells Charlie, steering him to a small, silver platform. "Stand right here."

Charlie stands on the platform.

"Ready?" the man asks, then hits some buttons, turns a key. Dry-ice smoke builds around Charlie. The platform, on hydraulics, jerks upward as a stereo kicks in, blaring Bon Jovi's "Livin' on a Prayer." "God damn, I love this song!" the man says. "Rock on!" He gives Charlie a thumbs-up.

Charlie rises through the floor of a small reception hall, smoke and laser lights dancing vulgarly around him like some old Siegfried and Roy show, minus the tigers. When the platform is level with the floor, the music, the lights, and the smoke stop. The room is empty, dim. The only light is from a flickering fluorescent bulb that casts a frail, blue glow over everything.

Charlie stands silent a moment then calls, "Hey." No one answers. The tables, naked, are turned on their sides, and the chairs stacked in the corner. A piñata in the shape of a monkey lays broken on the floor, pieces of stale candy scattered across the room. Charlie tries the doors but they are locked from the outside. There're no windows. He pounds on the doors. No one answers. "Hey!" he yells, stomping on the floor. The man doesn't reply.

Charlie searches the room, looking for something, anything to aid his escape. He finds a half empty bottle of butterscotch schnapps hidden under a pile of stained tablecloths. This is all a mistake, Charlie thinks. Curling up on the lift, Charlie wraps himself in a stained tablecloth and hits the bottle, hoping the sickly sweet taste of butterscotch doesn't make him vomit.

This is what he was trying to describe to the man: the locked room, the broken piñata, the dirty tablecloths. The sad barrenness of an expensive party being forgotten. This is what he wanted to say, what he wished to express. This room is how he feels.

Three days prior, Charlie was fired from his job. The specific reason why was never stated. His boss called him into his office after lunch, offered him a can of Diet Lemon Fanta. Charlie declined. "I have to let you go," his boss said, then called security to escort Charlie from the building. The can of Fanta was a kind gesture, Charlie thought, and he now wished he'd taken it, taken something to remember the place by.

When he got home, there was a letter from his mother waiting. Inside was a small newspaper clipping. His mother communicated to him via news clipping, articles from papers and magazines, all with post-it notes attached. It was a wedding announcement. It listed the reception hall. In looped handwriting that looked like dying balloons, his mother had written on a yellow post-it note: *Wasn't this your girl?*

Renee was getting married.

She'd moved to New York.

"It's okay," Charlie hears Simone say, then feels her fingers on his dry lips. He opens his eyes to find her hovering over him. He's outside, lying in the rowboat once filled with ice and shrimp. His suit jacket's gone. "What—"

"Glen's cool," she says. "That whole thing, his screaming, it's like a family"—she waves a hand—"seal of approval or something. He likes you," she adds. "You're golden with him."

"I need my friends," Charlie says, not knowing whom he's referring to. He's shaky, near ill, but no longer in the room with the rising platform. "I need to find Renee."

"Who's Renee, and why do you need to find her?" Simone asks.

"Because, I need—" Charlie breaks off. What do I need? he thinks, unable to answer. "I need my jacket," he finally tells her. "I need to go home."

"We've just begun," Simone says, looking better, softer, in the late afternoon light.

He struggles to pull himself into a standing position. "Where's the fat guy?" he asks. "How did I get here?"

"The same old questions," she says, helping him stand. "The same old answers."

They clean off the remains of a bottle of Bombay gin she has, smoke some cigarettes, then walk out to the parking lot.

"I've got to go," Simone says, leaning against her car. "Mom and Glen and all. But they're leaving for their latest honeymoon tonight, driving down to Dollywood, Tennessee. Bluegrass music, the mountains, pecan logs. They love that countrified shit," she says. "I'll be on my own, first time ever." She lightly touches his chest. "What are you going to do?"

He thinks of Renee, thinks of continuing his search for her. He's here for a reason. It no longer matters. "Nothing," he tells her. "I'm doing nothing."

"We could take this elsewhere," Simone says, "wait until my parents leave then head there, start again."

Inside the Carmine Palace, laughter, applause, and music from the different receptions mingle and fight in the hall, spill out the front door. People mill about, wandering in and out.

"This is all a mistake," Charlie says, gaining a strange balance from the gins. "Do you even know my name?"

Simone presses against him. "Your license says Charlie," she says, then hands him his wallet, his keys, and his cigarettes. "Sorry," she says. "A bad habit I have with new boyfriends."

"I'm going to be honest," Charlie says. "I don't much like

myself today. I came here to—I don't know. I came here for a girl."

"I'm a girl," she says, then kisses him deeply.

Her lips taste of lime and lavender, a taste that pleasantly pours down his throat. He takes her by the waist and kisses her back, kisses her hard and recklessly, like the only air left in the world is that in her lungs.

"Okay," he says, breaking free after nearly five minutes. He studies her face, her eyes, and sees that this is what he needs to do. "Okay," he repeats.

Simone asks him to drive. She had too much to drink, she says. He's had too much to drink, too. Still, he takes the keys from her.

Sitting in the passenger's seat, she closes her eyes and says, "We should pick up some nachos." The day's shadows point toward the Atlantic, growing longer by the minute. Behind Charlie is the Carmine Palace, his lost jacket, and the setting sun.

Before him is the road that leads to Babylon.

Pulling the car from the parking space, he pauses where the lot meets the road. The view of the approaching traffic is blocked by the tall, brown hedges. Charlie leans forward but can't see the oncoming cars. It's too hard to see. Cars and trucks race past, tearing from one place to another.

"We should get some pizza pockets, too," Simone says, yawning. She kicks off her shoes, then places her head in Charlie's lap. "And tonic," she says, gazing up at him, "for all the vodka my mom has. You know, we have a pool," she says. "It's above ground, but still."

Looking down at her, Charlie thinks of marriage, of love, of committing a life to another. He came for a reason. "Really?" he asks, and lets off the brake.

"Really," she says, as they edge blindly forward.

Bearfoot (Monster Truck Series), 1999
Perry Vasquez
Recycled Havoline 10w-30
on Arches print paper
22" x 30"

THE NAMES IN THE CASE

david barringer

AFTER MY MOTHER'S FATHER DIED, from complications after an angioplasty, I was given a small suitcase, brown, solid, old, with a built-in lock. The case had been my grandmother's. Many years earlier, my grandmother had died from complications after two brain surgeries. She'd survived the first surgery and had a hinge put into a cut-out section of her skull to allow the surgeons present and future access. A year later, in 1980, the surgeons drained the fluid expanding against her brain. Post-surgery complications—perhaps a blood clot; there was no autopsy—killed her. I was ten when she died. When my grandfather died (in the hospital and, again, without autopsy), I was approaching thirty, married, father of two. I was in the hospital room with my mother and uncle (my mother's brother-in-law) when we removed my grandfather from the machines. He defied expectations by breathing on his own for what felt like days but might not have been more than an hour. He choked and gasped, unconsciously, until he lost his strength, suffocated, and died. My mother wept. My uncle cried. I did not. I'm not sure why. Perhaps I had made my peace with his life. I had come to Chicago on business several times over the past years and usually arranged a visit with my grandfather. I'd watched him beat the odds of his physical health (the consequences of decades of alcohol, red meat, and cigars) and survive, year after year, but I'd also watched him decline. I knew that he knew he was living on borrowed time because he would tell me. He had outlived his money. He had outlived his desire to live. He would offer me whiskey from nearly clear bottles he'd watered down, to conceal his drinking, and when I would decline, he would offer me twenty dollars, and I would have to accept or risk bruising his ego. Then he would tell me that he never expected to live this long, and I would slip the twenty-dollar bill into a junk drawer by the kitchen's rotary phone. He would give me cassette tapes of himself singing, the nightclub kind of crooning he'd always wanted — but never had the nerve — to do. He'd never read much I'd written, but he knew I was a writer, maybe hoped I'd make his life into a story, real or imagined. Someday, maybe I will. I still have the tapes he made for me. And I have the suitcase. The suitcase tag has my grandmother's name and address on it. The suitcase is heavy, sturdy, stitched, and reinforced with some kind of metal in its walls, with rounded rectangular edges. It resembles a brass musician's instrument case, vintage, impregnable, something that would withstand the rigors of life with a touring jazz band or, for that matter, with my grandfather, who, escaping creditors, moved his family across the country, from Illinois to Arizona and back again. My mother and her sister endured different schools nearly every other year. My grandfather had been a Merchant Marine, a pharmaceutical salesman, a bartender. He loved singing "Danny Boy" and sang for posterity on my wedding video. A badge bears the manufacturer's name, Skyway, in script metallic lettering and is glued beneath the locking mechanism. My grandmother's initials, V.J.Z., are embossed in faded silver below that. Skyway, founded in 1910, is still in business.

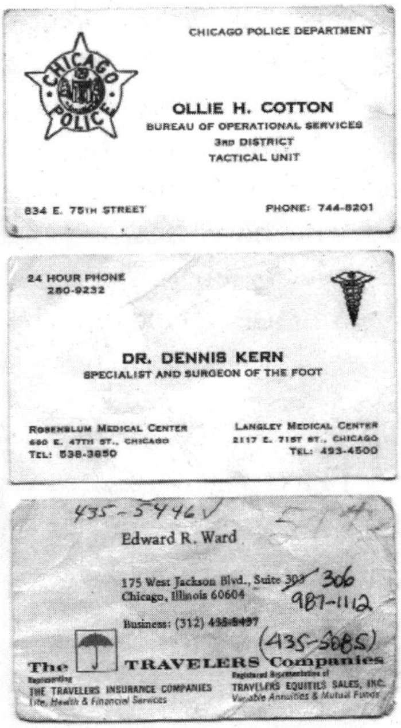

It appears to be a woman's traveling case. On the inner lid are two puffy elastic pockets of the same deep-purple material as the lining. These two pockets embrace an otherwise loose, removable cosmetic mirror. An inventory of the odds and ends inside reveals: an old smudged lock, without its key, made by the Independent Lock Company of Fitchburg, Mass.; interlocked rings of tarnished keys; the two suitcase keys, miniatures as if for a doll's house, on a safety pin; a cheap glass ashtray rimmed in some thin metal, maybe tin; a stack of unused holiday cards with pink elephants on their covers; five family photographs, color, including one of my grandfather, myself, and my year-old daughter, a photo that memorializes the only time my grandfather ever met one of my kids; a Monaco cigar box of assorted matchbooks, including ones from Full House in Hanover Park, Great Godfrey Daniels in Skokie, Up Down Tobacco Shop in Chicago, The Parthenon in Chicago's Greektown, and the Playboy Clubs of Buffalo and St. Louis, these latter matchbooks being manufactured in Chicago; a strange letter from a family friend or relative; two letters, printed out by computer and stapled, from the organizer of my grandfather's 60th high-school reunion, who typed, to everyone, "I was going to say, 'Be good,' but at your age, I know you are being good," and who handwrote, to my grandfather, "We missed you. Hang on for our 65th or 62nd!"); and, finally, a small ivory snapshut case, a clock inset atop its lid.

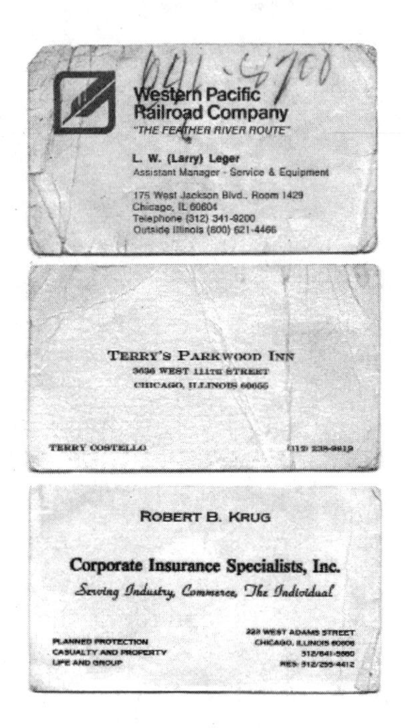

This last case appears to be a jewelry case, or perhaps it is intended to secure the bedside necessities of a traveler: glasses, earrings, pen, etc. The case is narrower than a paperback and heavier than a bible. On the clock's face, which is tinted an ugly, nostalgic olive gold, is printed, "New Haven." The back of the clock protrudes into the inner lid. The knobs allow for winding the clock and adjusting the time; there is no wake-up alarm. Inside the case are: cufflinks; a plastic nametag with Joe, my grandfather's first name, engraved on it; a black button; two ball bearings; a costume-jewelry pin; two tiny nuts fallen from the tiny screws securing the clock to the lid; a black-bead necklace with a cross of Jesus Christ (my grandmother was Polish Catholic); a nickel-sized pin from the Chicago Bartenders Union AFL-CIO Local 278 (my grandfather used to tend bar in the John Hancock building, among other places); and a haphazard collection of business cards, collected, presumably, by my grandfather.

312-252-9268
Norton's Mens Wear
SPECIALISTS IN TALL AND BIG MEN'S APPAREL
GREGORY METSIG
2959 MILWAUKEE AVENUE
CHICAGO, ILL. 60618

JOHN A. GAUGHAN
PORTABLE TOOL SALES AND SERVICE, INC.

NUMISCO, INC.
RARE COIN DEALERS
NUMISMATIC INVESTMENTS
ERV BESKOW
1423 W. FULLERTON
CHICAGO, IL 60614
312 528-8800
TELEX 25-6219
800 621-1339

It is these cards, finally, that interest me. They suggest a history of relationships, a past peopled by acquaintances and friends about whom I know nothing. I never met any of them. Some may be men my grandfather knew well in his social circle or briefly, perhaps for a single night, as a bartender. They are insurance representatives and doctors, salesmen and relatives. (One card is my own, but I'm not counting that one.) I have always wanted to somehow catalog these twenty-seven cards, to arrange them in a way that suggests an impression of my grandfather's past or even, I admit it, an evocation of the past in general. The cards are skeletal and random at best, underequipped for the documentary task I want to impose upon them. Still, I record some because what else can I do with them? They are enclosed inside a case within a case, and no one else, now, is struck with the impulse to preserve them. Listing them is a poor substitute for the experience of fingering through them, one at a time, comparing age and wear, the typography, the scribbled notes on their white spaces and backsides. Men handed these cards to my grandfather. Under what circumstances? How many of these men meant something to my grandfather? Are these men (they are invariably men, judging by the names) living or dead? More than a mere twenty-seven men must have handed my grandfather their business cards during his many years as a bartender, let alone his entire life. So why did he keep these particular cards? A couple are obviously the doctors he was seeing at the end of his life. But others are just as obviously decades old, stained, pocked, cut, as translucent as skin. Look at their jobs, the companies they worked for, their names. What lives did these men lead? How many of them kept my grandfather's card? Did my grandfather even have a card? There is more I can say, but perhaps this catalog and its exegesis only have meaning for me. And what is that meaning anyway? And if I ever define that private meaning in any definite way, how can I convey something of it to anyone else? Most grandsons receive a portion of their grandfather's personal effects, left to them intentionally or, in my case, unintentionally. These are business cards that happened to be in the possession of my grandfather, that happened to be locked in my grandmother's Skyway luggage. These are names in a case, orphans on my doorstep, people from a past that is theirs to know and mine to imagine. It is imagination, I think, that is stirred up by these cards, these bare records of men my grandfather knew. Never intended as epitaphs, they are something else. They are something that makes me heartsick to live only one life, to be denied so much history, to have only one name to give.

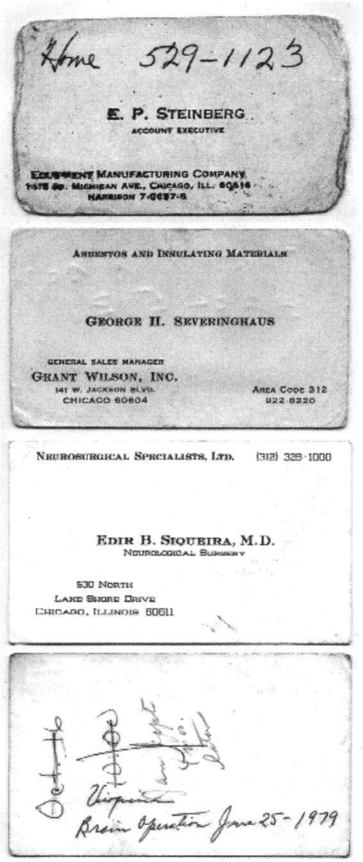

winner: 2005 ann arbor book festival short story contest
judged by jonathan ames

A Love Story

ginny mackenzie

George and I have moved into the chocolate-covered-cherry factory—well, not exactly into it—into the loft above it. Although the candy-makers no longer occupy the building, we still smell the cream filling and the shiny, dark chocolate that once dropped down over each small, breast-shaped cherry. Waiting to tuck them into their individual beds of silver and red foil, female candy-makers, dressed in lace-trimmed blue dresses, once looked out over them as if they were the products of a radiant meteor shower. They would grab each one gently as it rolled toward them and fit them into elegant white boxes to be shipped to specialty stores. I had lived near the cherry factory even before I married George, my third husband, had toured it many times, and, finally, my wish to be even closer to those delicious smells has been fulfilled. Unfortunately, the cherry factory went out of business just before we moved in. But, back when it was still in operation, the cooks and packers would eat their lunches on the factory stoop where, upon seeing Paulie, our young son, one of them would go inside and sneak him out a box of chocolates. We were among the first families to move into the commercial food district, and the factory workers treated Paulie like their own child. And it suited us to treat the factory as our own. It was the smell of chocolates that brought me out of a sleep hangover every morning and helped me make the transition into the city angst.

George is an English professor who also writes grammar textbooks. He has to—adjunct professors get paid so badly, and George doesn't have the people skills to ever get tenure. So I take care of George, and, sometimes, I paint. Along with other artists, we live secretly in one of the city's illegal artists' neighborhoods zoned for commercial use only. This, of course, all precedes what occurred with the arrival of the tall man, who came to see us not so very long ago. I think now his behavior was all a ruse to plant himself in our modest lives for what is turning out to feel like eternity. I still don't know what it was about him that made me want to give my life away.

But, as I've said, the factory itself has closed, though, occasionally, I see one of the candy-workers entering the building, dressed in her regulation blue-and-white dress with a lace pocket over the right breast. I tell George, "They look like 18th century romantic poets." George says, "They look inconsequential." The truth is somewhere in between. Tonight, however, we're living our own inconsequential lives during one of the city's warmest summer nights ever. George is eating, or, more accurately, gulping down his dinner at the kitchen table, like he often does. We aren't speaking. When he finishes, he lays down his napkin, scrapes the floor as he pushes his chair from the table, smiles somewhat defiantly, and goes into the living room. All of this is per usual. And I follow him per usual. After taking our seats, the same seats we always take, a few feet from each other, we sit there breathing in our after-dinner contentment. George picks up a book he's been reading, opens it, shuts it, and puts it back on the shelf. I pretend to read one of my own.

What happens then is that, in one of his rare verbal appearances, George announces, as clearly as the sound of coins hitting the floor, "I don't intend to leave this building anymore—starting tonight." This, understandably, hurts me, since we're so inextricably linked. I don't really understand his dismay with life, other than his frustration with his writing. He's always saying, "I'm a hack. I'm just not good enough, that's all." I don't know what it is he feels he's not good enough at, so I never know what to say.

"You just go ahead and do that," I say. "But what are you going to do for money?"

"I won't eat," he says. "Why get angry? Why take it that way?" he says.

George loves asking questions.

"Do you want to join me?" he says.

That was George only a short two years ago. I have joined him, of course, because I love him; I can't imagine doing otherwise. However, I feel the need to relate the incident, to comment on the suddenness of our conjoining and the extent of my present embarrassment, though, at times, I must admit, I find aspects of it entertaining—even convivial. We've both been here in the living room pretty much since that August evening. I wish I could say I see an end to it, but my first allegiance is to George, my extremely insignificant other, for whom I'd sacrifice myself at a moment's notice. And George appears dedicated to his isolation. It has become his raison d'être.

Although, as I've said, I'm on my third marriage, this is only George's first. Sometimes I think of myself as a woman of a certain age, and I should be grateful to have George. Neither of us wants to cause Paulie pain, so we have a lot of motivation to be happy. Paulie, thank God, is a good kid. This makes me feel lucky. In fact, I feel lucky for a lot of things: I'm still quite pretty, I think—familiar eyes, modest-red hair, an appealing figure. And when George holds my hand, it's like nothing else. He inches his hand toward mine, brushes it casually against mine for some time as we walk, before finally enclosing my palm in his, intertwining his fingers with mine. It's as if our hands are making love. We're part of the same history. Sometimes, in fact, George is more me than me.

Most endearing of all, George knows what I'm thinking; he has his eyes on me even when I sleep. "Real men," I tell him, "are not afraid to give themselves away." Every time I leave my chair for even a minute to look out the window or peer through the peephole into the hall, George knows it. It's such a disappointment to me when no one is out there. I have hopes one of the candy women, with her gold hairnet and red lips, will come up here out of curiosity, and she'll be standing in front of our door just as I'm looking out the peephole. However, there's never anyone there, and I seem to be the only one who believes any of the workers still enter the building. But George says, "I've seen branches coming out the window, loaded with cherries." I believe him; it gives me hope. Perhaps the cherry pits have taken root in the factory floor, and little cherry trees are growing in there, their cramped branches struggling to get to the sun. They may even have strangled the cooks and consumed the girls who wrap the candies. No one, of course, would think to check out such things; there is simply nothing in it for them.

So there he is. My love. Sitting on the couch, looking, at the moment, like a squashed bug. His figure isn't as attractive as mine, but his hair is softer, fuller, darker than mine, though it has no shine and sometimes appears dead. Still, he compensates for its rigor mortis when he brushes it, reminding me of a Springer Spaniel I once had — the more you brushed him, the more beautiful he became; I remember how he pranced around when we said, good boy! When George brushes his hair, which he must do five or six times a day, it's then the whole room jumps, which doesn't require much of a leap of the imagination, considering the weight of our furniture — lamps, chairs, dresser — everything is made from summers of driftwood collecting.

Still, two years is a long time, and so much has happened since George first decided he wouldn't go out; it's hard to know what deserves the most attention. The first year, George's mood progressed into a deeper and darker persona, and I never knew what to expect. He seemed to need to withdraw from the world, and I had no choice but to go along with him. I remained dumbfounded, rather numb, I think. Then, during the second year, I looked out into the hall through the peephole, as I did every morning, searching for signs of life. But that particular morning, after initially following the shadowy angles into the dark brown niches leading to the locked doors that led to the cherry factory, I thought I saw movement. While I was surveying the shadows, my eye aching from such careful inspection, a man appeared, walking toward our door. I tell you, he appeared out of nowhere and, of all things, he was carrying a small, shorthaired dog under one arm. When he got to our door, he paused, set the dog down, and brought his fist up until it was nearly in my eye. Then, gently, from the feel of it, he gave three small raps on the door. I turned to see if George had heard it, but he was in the living room, obviously lost in a dream of success. Why I opened the door to this man still perplexes me. Normally, I'm a cautious, even fearful, person. Maybe it was that anyone carrying a dog couldn't be a crazed drug addict; a murderer wouldn't knock on the door; a polite rapist was an oxymoron. Besides, how many visitors did we get a year — other than delivery boys dropping off food or messengers returning George's manuscripts? Without even hooking the chain first, I opened the door wide, an action that invited the tall man with the small dog into our loft. He stood there staring at me and then at his dog, then back at me. He looked tired and hot.

"Who are you looking for?" I asked.

"I've had a terrible time finding you. Are you Rebecca and George?"

"Well, I'm the Rebecca part," I said. "What do you want? If you're looking for the candy factory, it's been closed a long time." Perhaps, I thought, he knew something—I would ask him if he happened to notice, having just come from the outside world, whether cherry blossoms were pushing at the windows of the factory. Maybe powerful, young cherry trees had forced open the windows, and vines were curling down the sides of the building, causing the factory to take on the appearance of a courthouse or library. The very fact that he was here meant he knew his way around the neighborhood. I couldn't wait to talk to him.

"I went to a lot of buildings, asked a lot of people if they knew you, but they said they didn't or, more often, they shut the door in my face. They treated me like an annoyance. I don't think I'm an annoyance."

"No one knows us. We're the hidden community. What do you want?" I was beginning to understand why people thought him an annoyance. To make things worse, I was sure George was asleep on the other side of the wall, and I didn't want to wake him. Just then, the tall man adjusted an old-fashioned pair of glasses up over the bridge of his nose; he was rather good-looking, with a formal look about him, a learned look. Probing, intelligent eyes. I wondered if he was a colleague of George's.

"I'm sorry to bother you," he said. "I just had to tell you how much your marriage means to someone like me. I've been single my entire life, never felt enough for a woman to think I could stand her year after year. You and George have what we all want. I hope you'll talk to me about it. Is your husband home?"

I couldn't understand what possible misinformation had brought a man to our door who thought us a model couple, and such a milk sop at that; he wasn't capable of slamming a door. When George wants something, he just says, "Pass the bloody salt, Rebecca." No preemptive warning, just, "...that is, if you think you can reach your arm all the way to the end table there; do you think you can manage that, or are you too exhausted from sitting there all day?" As if he's busy, out earning a living or something, as if he can't roll his ass over here and reach the salt himself. At the very least he could make it worth my while; why should I disturb my thoughts just so he can salt his oatmeal? And what oatmeal: crusted over, as dead as the Bay of Naples. I tell him what happens in Naples. For one thing, they don't rely on other people to straighten out their messes.

"Do you know," I told the tall man, motioning him to a chair, "that, in Naples, an alarm sounds when the water of the Adriatic enters the waterfront, and people have only two hours to carry out their rugs and put their furniture on blocks. That's all the warning they get. If they don't hear the siren and happen to sleep through it, they awaken to water in their beds and rats in the room. I've told George this. I'd like to see what he would do if he saw a rat in here. He knows I wouldn't react, but he's such a baby. Maybe that's what it would take, a 20-pound wet rat scurrying through the place, to get him to move... I told him, 'We can't stay here forever, George... I can't salt your oatmeal for the rest of your life.' But, then, I'm sure you're not interested in all this. Do you happen to know anything about the candy factory? Do you ever see anyone going in it?"

"I'm not from this neighborhood. I did see a light on though, a little light in a round window. It looked like a cathedral light."

"It must be the light from the Pre-Raphaelite girl," I said, anxious to hear more details. "Do you think there's someone in there making love? Do you think that's it? I mean, that's your subject, right? Love? That's where your expertise lays. You know, I've always thought George was a bit like the Mediterranean. It's too small of a body of water for the moon and sun's gravity, so it has no tide; the Strait of Gibraltar moves its water. Once the Atlantic passes through the Strait, its saline water swirls around the basin and rushes in on top of the outflow, which is the denser and saltier

Mediterranean. That's what I am — the Atlantic Ocean rushing in over George's lagoon — made saltier, of course — by the fact that I'm so efficient, to begin with, at getting the damn salt over there to him. But I fear I'm becoming mean-spirited."

The tall man bent over and set his dog down on the hardwood floor. "I'm Rex Madison, and, yes, I'm an author too. George's agent said you two might talk to me about marriage. I'm writing a book called *Marriage: The World's Twelfth Oldest Profession.*" Rex put out his hand, and I shook it. Dog hairs flew off his shirt. "Have I come at a bad time?"

"I don't feel like I'm a good candidate for discussing the secrets of marriage. And talking to George has become, well, like talking to the wallpaper, or the couch, which is, in fact, where he's at right now — sleeping on the couch. But at least I've begun to know why he sits there. And I'm willing to talk about that," I said, though, now, I think I was too cavalier. "George says, 'Rebecca, get the salt.' 'Rebecca, turn out the light.' Rebecca this... Rebecca that. I tell him I'm the sea and it'll take me 80 years to turn over all my water and that because he's the Mediterranean and easy to pollute, whatever gets dumped in him stays there a long, long time. I tell him the Mediterranean is so filthy, they fish dead cows out of it." After that, I felt calmer and decided I shouldn't say so much to this man, who I knew nothing about. "Nothing dislodges George. Sooner or later, we'll run out of credit cards for food. What then?" The small dog looked as if it was about to pee, but, right on schedule, we heard George. "See, he watches me all the time. He knows you're here. But George has his moments. He definitely has his moments. And, after all, I'm a woman of a certain age."

"Maybe I've come at a bad time. I can come back," Rex said, looking like he wanted to sit down. Or maybe he needed to pee too.

"Sometimes I don't take it. I say, 'You know, George, I'm more than just a little tired of this. I have a delicate ecosystem, which it's taken me years to create. Think of me as the city of Troy. Troy once sat at the mouth of the Dardanelles, and today it looks out at a landlocked plain. That's what happens when sediment fills a harbor. Troy wasn't finished off by the Greeks, George; it was made useless when it lost its harbor.'... Do you know what he says to that?"

"I can't imagine," Rex said, looking only mildly interested.

As we walked into the living room, I continued, "He says, 'Rebecca, you're full of the god-damnedest, dumbest metaphors I've ever heard.' That's what he says."

When we reached the living room, George had his hand deep in a package of chipped ham. Some of it was hanging out of his other hand. It looked like pink spaghetti or birthday streamers, and I couldn't resist saying, "You're the landlocked harbor, George, the sediment, the curse of Troy."

"And who are you?" George asked, looking at Rex and putting down his meat. But he'd obviously heard our conversation.

"I'm Rex Madison. Your agent thought I should talk to you. I'm writing a book about marriage. He said I should talk to you and your wife."

"Yes. Rebecca and I have a splendid marriage. Don't we, Rebecca? She's an incurable romantic. We love living here alone, calling out for food. I'd be happy seeing only Becky here for the rest of my life. It's true we would make an inexhaustible subject for someone interested in the nature of commitment. But I'm not sure I want to share that with just anyone."

"The weather gets on George's nerves," I said, "particularly the heat; one would think he wouldn't care any longer, but when a humid breeze blows through the front window, he says it wilts him. But when he says he loves me, I feel a shaky sensation in my knees. Then, night falls, and I forget about the weather and about the feelings I have for him. What choice do I have?" But when I next looked at Rex, I saw that little leaves surrounded his chair; tendrils had slipped under the door and were shooting up the sides of his chair. I wondered if George saw them.

Rex and his dog were sharing the armchair; he had a way, I noticed, of making his subjects feel comfortable, in fact, of making them forget he was there. "I know you get up and go into the bedroom at night, George," I said. "I don't hear you, but I know you do. I know you look out the window and see other people. Don't you see that other men have jobs, that they support their wives?"

"Listen to this!" George was speaking. He had a postcard in his hand. "'Say hello to Rebecca.' That's what it says, not 'Hi, George, Say hello to Rebecca'... just, 'Say hello to Rebecca.'"

"I never bother George," I said, remembering Rex, "when he talks about the mail. It's only right that he gets to read it, being a writer. Did you know he's writing a cookbook for golfers called *Greens: Fabulous Recipes for Those Below Par*? It's a humor book, isn't it George?"

"The last time I checked," George said, putting on that know-it-all attitude he's so good at.

I had begun to feel queasy. If I looked into the hall, would it be filled with vines? Cherry trees? Did I even want to know?

"Look Becky, this postcard from the Powells... what nice pastel shades for the beach umbrellas, and the people on the beach—though somewhat dated—are quite attractive."

I looked at Rex, who didn't seem to notice the vine by his foot. "When George reads the mail to me, the air smells cool and sweet," I said, "like leaves in the fall, or a really expensive salad."

Rex had finished the sandwich George gave him and had fallen asleep in the armchair. George was also nodding off. He looked like a little boy, like he did when he moved in next door to me when he was ten and very unhappy—mostly, I think, because his dad was such a drunk. People said he drank a bottle of scotch a day and told people it was scotch and water, though no one ever caught him putting any water in it. Thank goodness, George wasn't a drunk. I was soon pulled out of my reverie, however, by the sound of Rex's dog scratching at the door. George woke up, too, and Rex excused himself to take his dog for a walk. Neither of them commented on the leafy vines that had slid under the corner of the door, so perhaps it was unimportant. I decided not to bring it up. The door thudded shut behind him, and I thought I glimpsed a bird with a cherry in its beak fly past the door. Perhaps a candymaker had left the window open and a bird had flown in.

"How about some music, George, some soft chords?" I asked. I switched on the radio and turned to the mellow station. In time with the music I let my arms swing in lazy circles on either side of my chair and pretended I was spinning in the middle of a softly-lit dance hall; George was wearing a white tuxedo. Glenn Miller was playing "Little Brown Jug."

"You look like Paulie," I told George, "like he did when he didn't know whether to tell us he stole money from the coin can. Remember? When he finally confessed, you punished him so severely, he didn't speak to us for a week. What was it you made him do?"

George, yawning like he just remembered his life, said, "Made him wash every car on the block for free, that's what. Made him a saint to the neighbors. They tried to pay him, but I wouldn't let him accept any money. I remember." But then he seemed to forget all about our history and about Paulie. "Your arms are so white and smooth, Rebecca. They don't have a vein showing. That's very good, you know. I like it when you wear that pink and white see-through nightgown; it's the color you are in the night light when I kiss you and you flush a little before you kiss me back."

I wished Rex had been there to hear George at his best, and, to top it off, I wasn't sure he'd be back. Glenn Miller was no longer playing, and a song played in my head, a song I could no longer remember the words to, but it felt gentle and neutral, and it made me feel George looked sexy, or, at least, possible.

George wasn't what I'd hoped for, but I was too far into it. The days had begun to feel creaky and uncertain, like the end of summer. Our youth was slipping and I remembered, as a child, how I gripped the rope of the barn swing so hard, I felt that if I left go, I'd have to stay a child forever. All I could think about then was growing up and taking care of the good things around me: the chickens and cows and cornfields. And George, of course; I needed a George. And, now, not only did I have George, I had a cherry factory.

"What do you think happened to Rex? Do you think he's all right?" I asked George. Rex was missing the best part, the part most like the real us, the way we were when we first met. George and I. "Don't think I don't appreciate you, George. I do."

"You make it sound like I'm yeast rising. Would you like to put your toes in my dough?" George said. He was starting to get into it; I liked that. "Would you like to knead me in a bowl of something pretty enough to eat?"

"I don't know what you mean, George. Is this your way of asking me to make love to you? Because I can do that, George."

"Everyone can do that, Rebecca."

"Not everyone, George."

"I give you purpose," George said, holding my hand. He seemed to be studying the lines in my palms, my nails, the ellipses that topped the fleshy tips of my fingers.

"I'd like to suck your fingers, George. Look out the window. There's an El Greco moon out tonight. I want to have you right here. Under the El Greco moon." I imagined myself carrying a parasol, perfumed like the bank of an inland sea. But then I heard Rex at the door. I opened it and Rex came in and set down his little dog. "This," I told the tall man, as I looked longingly at our entwined hands, "is what happiness feels like. We're like two albino deer in the snow. We blend. We're what nature intended."

"Can I quote you on that?" the tall man asked. When I

looked at him and heard those words, I didn't realize they were to be the last words I would hear from him. All that came out of his mouth after that were birds. There must have been a dozen of them. They were chirping—no, twittering, like an orchestra, perfectly in tune. It seemed very natural.

"Someone was here tonight, George. Someone who thought we could tell him the secret of love. Do you think we know? About love? George, dance with me, dance with me right here in the living room."

"Living room?" George asked, sounding suspicious. "Are you using that word as one word or two?"

"I know living room is two words; you've told me that. And fish bone is two words, George. But I'm not sure about back porch."

"Back porch is two words, always two words."

"You're so sexy when you talk about grammar, George. Will you let the Atlantic slosh against the walls of the Mediterranean tonight? Will we hear the Dardanelles crash?"

"English, Rebecca. Speak English."

"But you know that's why I want you to read the mail, George. I can see every color and nuance when you read it. Dance with me, George."

"And who will play the piano if I'm dancing?"

"We'll play it together in our heads. Wear your tuxedo. George, please, let's do it once before we die."

This was the best part, and, still, Rex didn't materialize. He was missing the best part, the part most like the real us, the way we were when we first met. I guess we were just too much for him. George and I. George knew how to penetrate my very soul. "There's something in you that gets sweeter in the dark," I told George, though I was looking at all the foliage that was growing on the ceiling. Vines covered the bed and were headed for the kitchen. "Dance with me, George."

"O. K. Baby, what the hell..."

"But first," I said, "I'll take a bath. I want to feel fresh." I left George to go into the bathroom to fill the tub. The water sloped against the sides when I stepped in, and I sat down, just straight enough that my breasts were out of the water. I needed my breasts to be totally out of the water. George had come into the bathroom and had his soapy hand on my back; I could feel how full of thought he was. And I was singing, but very softly, *Little Brown Jug, how I love thee.* And I was happy, as if George was all I yearned for, and he was taking care of me and washing my back and underarms. And he was wearing a white tuxedo that was getting splashed, but he didn't care — and he was saying, "My lovely pink wife."

100 Krones

doug hoekstra

It is 1967 and I am high up in the center field bleachers at Wrigley Field. From my vantage point, I check my scorecard to confirm that it is, indeed, Curt Flood playing centerfield for the Cardinals. He crouches in suspense, alert and ready to pounce, glove open, bare right hand extended, his uniform a striking contrast of red and white against the sharp green backdrop of the outfield grass. The pitcher winds and delivers, there is the sharp crack of the bat and although I can barely pick up the ball against the pale blue sky, Flood tracks it from the start. The ball is rising, hurling towards the right-field gap and he races towards it, effortlessly, smooth and fluid. It quickly becomes clear that he is sure to catch the ball, despite the odds against him and the trajectory of the ball, ascending quickly like a missile shot from a rocket launcher. The ball is heading towards the very top of the vine covered wall, right by the yellow 400 foot sign, a sure double or cheap home run, but Flood times his leap perfectly, the small white projectile landing solidly in his mitt as if part of a synchronized ballet. I register the out F-8, with a circle and exclamation point.

Curt Flood soon becomes famous for challenging the Lords of Baseball, writing the Commissioner a letter that, among other things, tells him and the world that "After twelve years in the major leagues, I do not feel that I am a piece of property to be bought and sold irrespective of my wishes." He sits out an entire year, at the height of his career, to let the matter play out in court and when he returns, he isn't the same player. Flood won't just pay lip service to his principles, he will put it all on the line and sacrifice his career, and all the players who followed in his wake owe him a debt of gratitude. On and off the field of play, he makes the impossible possible.

Three years later, I was on a plane headed for Denmark, trying desperately to sleep, to somehow outrun jet lag. I was due to land in the early morning, and I figured if I slept on the plane, I would be able to hit the ground running. But it never really works that way - crammed into economy class, I took my sleeping pills and wrapped myself in a blanket and stared glassy eyed out the window. I popped in and out of semi-sleep, with lines of spittle and fractured dreams making me feel worse than if I hadn't slept at all.

This was my first trip to Europe and I had mixed feelings about the whole thing. As the plane descended, I looked out the window at a flat, green countryside, devoid of hills, heavily graced with farmland. It reminded me of long stretches of Iowa or Illinois, where cornfields meet dairy farms and the curves of the earth roll up and down like gentle ocean waves.

I've always considered myself an American's American, I loved baseball, my parents were first generation, and all the best rock and roll that ever was, was born in America. But fate has a way of twisting things around your finger and, sure enough, while at college I met Elsie, and she became the magnet to pull me across the ocean. We met during senior year, two English majors who got to know each other by trading our writing back and forth. Her grammar wasn't perfect, but her English was much better than my Danish (which had gone from non-existent to primeval through our relationship) and more than that, her prose dripped with soul. I could construct a sentence, but she could make it breathe, and I fell in love with the girl who felt those things. I was shocked, hooked, and a bit intimidated.

We dated all year, and the summer after, and then she moved back to Denmark. Still carrying that unique blend of arrogance and insecurity found in most men just out of college, I was surprised—not only was I charming and sensitive, she could pick up a green card in the deal as extra credit, assuming we headed down the pathway to love and marriage. So, when she headed home, I poured over the possibilities and realized that the simplest reason was probably the most accurate, that her enthusiasm for her native land was great, and, after all, home is a powerful thing.

"You don't understand," she said one time, as we were waiting for the el to pick us up at Fullerton, the stop outside campus. The wind was blowing hard and it was freezing cold, the kind of bone-chilling hell-raising subzero bitterness so special to Chicago. "You live in a young country; there are many things that are beautiful here, but as a people, you are so young."

"I know we're young," I said quickly, my words running together, "but there are good things here because of that. We are fresh, I mean, artistically, America is...."

There was a pause and she shook her head sadly, or so it seems now, looking back. I distinctly remember her staring past me at the pigeons that dared to land bravely on the frozen rooftops across from our stop. Our generation was at the forefront of a cultural revolution, heading from the sixties into an even better decade ahead.

Elsie was from Copenhagen, a city that dates back to 1167, and as she also reminded me, Denmark as a country was settled 10,000 years ago, when the ice retreated from Scandinavia. The ice never fully retreated from Elsie, but that made her all that much more mysterious. She was slightly shorter than I, but with heels, we'd meet straight on, and I'd lose my footing, envying her deep blue eyes and her implacable personality. She was an old soul, just as comfortable in that moment, in that setting, as she would be at some class function in a pretentious loft, or at breakfast at the Melrose, or in the stifling heat of the bleachers at Wrigley Field, where I'd taken her to her first baseball game.

"Why do you write everything down," she'd asked me, as I meticulously scored the game. "I just always have," I answered, "it keeps me in the game." "Do you look at it later?" "Of course," I said. "I save them all. Tonight, I'll take out my baseball men, and replay the game." I felt Elsie's body stiffen next to me, and I quickly reassured her that I was joking. Her body softened, but she paused ever so slightly before changing the course of the conversation. This was another part of her personality; sometimes the pauses were happy, other times, they had a feeling of sadness. But they always unsettled me just a little bit.

And so when I landed in Denmark, Elsie was waiting for me and we wandered through an ancient city full of canals, wide boulevards, and vast public parks and gardens. The people were friendly and open, and seemingly devoid of conflict. Though I was an outsider, I soon grew comfortable. Perhaps it was because I was accompanied by a native who was familiar with the pace and rubbed off on me, making me feel the same — or perhaps it was simply the inherent nature of the people.

"See how friendly everyone is," she said to me, as we sat at a canal-side café, with our tea and biscuits. "People are not in such a hurry here."

"That's true," I added, "but there's not as much to do."

She looked at me as if I'd personally, and purposely, insulted her people, her clan of Rasmussens, descendants of the ancient peoples. I couldn't help it, I let out a smile and she rolled her eyes and flipped a piece of her biscuit at me.

"Just because there's no baseball doesn't mean there's nothing to do."

"Yeah, well, you know," I said with a whisper, "everyone's so mellow because they're all the same. Everyone's blue blue blue, just like you!"

"Not all like me," she said, most seriously, "there are many foreign nationals."

"Yes, but they're all white," I said.

"I thought you said we were blue."

We walked along the Long Line where the harbor meets the Sound. It was a beautiful sunny day and the clouds dotted the sky in perfect harmony, as if the steady hand of a master painter had strategically placed them. The air smelled fresh, and it carried the sea with it everywhere. Rows of houses painted bright colors led one down the street, guide markers that flashed a different sign, door-to-door. Her arm was hooked around mine and she wore one of those knit berets that were fashionable at the time. She pointed out places where she'd been as a little girl, with her parents. We came to a statue of a mermaid and she said, "Oh, let me take your picture with the Mermaid." I stood and she clicked and I paused for another moment to take in the statue. "Is this by some famous Danish sculptor?," I asked.

"Well, I don't know about famous..." she said, pausing, "but that's from Hans Christian Andersen."

" I didn't know that."

"You have never heard of Hans Christian Andersen," she frowned. "Didn't your parents read you his stories as a child?"

"Did he do Hansel and Gretel? I said "That one used to scare the shit out of me."

"No, no, no, this is the Little Mermaid. You know, it is the story of a shipwrecked prince who sets off on a perilous quest to win his love. To become a human she must give up her voice and her mermaids tail, but if the prince should wed another, she will turn into foam on the sea and disappear forever."

"Wow, that's a great story."

"Yes," she sad, sadly. "And very romantic..."

I stayed with her and her parents in Amager, a marshy suburb of Copenhagen near the airport, just southeast of the main city. They were very gracious and open-minded, I thought, since we shared her bedroom, though we weren't even engaged. My senses were reeling with new sights and sounds and food, and experiences but after about a week, I began to get bored. It wasn't Elsie; it was the routine of doing nothing. I journaled and mapped out ideas for stories to write, but I couldn't bear doing any heavy writing at the time. It seemed as if everything I was doing was somehow connected to what I'd do when I got back to the States. And, yet, I had no plans to return — my ticket was one way and we had decided to just "see how things went."

One morning, as we walked through the heart of the city, I saw a little blonde-haired boy and his father come out of a houseboat, jumping up and down as they stepped onto the street to head for some unknown adventure. The father wore a fisherman's cap, more style than occupation, and they hustled off in the opposite direction from which we walked. Couples like us strolled by and we paused now and again to take in whatever sight took our fancy. We made it to Tivioli Gardens and I was struck by something unusual, the sight of a black man with a jaunty black beret and wisp of goatee sketching tourists and passer-bys. He had several landscapes laid out in front of him and we wandered over to look at them. There was one of the Little Mermaid statue and I thought of buying it for Elsie, but she quickly followed me, ruining the surprise, though not the possibility. I said hello to the man, in Danish (the only words I knew, along with thank you) and he nodded, sketching ahead.

"You an American?" he said, in English.

I thought he must be as well. "Yes, I am."

"How come you're not in Vietnam?" he asked. "You look to be about the age."

I was taken aback by his comment, stark and direct. Sure, my folks had money, and I had been in college, and had been able to avoid the draft, so far. Like most young men at the time, I thought about what I'd do if my number did come up—I didn't believe in the war, and I felt it didn't deserve anyone's sacrifice. But I didn't feel like discussing it with strangers.

"I like the weather here better," I joked.

He stopped sketching and smiled. "Well, so do I, brother so do I, so do I." He appeared quite fit for a painter, well-muscled arms belying the trade. "Yeah," he said slowly, "the weather is nice and mild over here."

"Are you from the states?" I continued.

"Oakland. You?"

"Chicago."

"Welcome to Copenhagen, my friend. Is this your lady?"

"Yes it is."

"You're quite a lucky man, to not be in Vietnam and to be with this lady. If I were you," he said, stroking his goatee and looking at her warmly, "I'd marry her and stay here."

I changed the subject and asked him how many Krones for the painting of the Little Mermaid.

"What do you think the market will bear?

"I don't know; I mean, do you sell a lot of paintings?

"I do okay. You know, it's just like, what is something worth to you, that's the question. Like, if you're an American and you get drafted, is it worth it to you to give up this wonderful woman to go to Vietnam and shoot people you don't even know? Or is it worth it to you to give up your citizenship and live here in peace? If a man has a prized possession, a gold watch his grandfather gave him, and he goes to pawn it, what is it worth? You dig?"

He was talking in circles as far as I was concerned, and I remember feeling incredibly drawn and repelled, interested and impatient. I remember the overriding thought I had was that I just wanted to buy a painting, not a lecture.

"Listen, man," he said, "It's good to see a boy from home

hanging over here. If you and your lady can spare a few, I'll do a sketch of you together. I'm more of a landscape man, but I'll give it a crack. I'll only charge you 100 krones. Whaddya say?"

Elsie had been watching us silently. "Oh, let's do it," she said, "We can sit down right here against the stone wall. How's that?" 100 krones was cheap and I wondered how the guy was making it.

"You heard the lady," our displaced painter said. "You better listen to her, my friend."

We sat down on the ground, leaning back against the wall. I put my arm around Elsie and the sketch man worked quickly, glancing up and down to his pad, drawing quick broad strokes, smooth and fluid. He used charcoal on paper, and within fifteen minutes, he was done. He proudly showed us the result and it was immediately clear that he knew what he was doing. Sure, it looked like us, but with Elsie, he captured something deeper, the essence of the reserves she had that lie in wait beyond the obvious beauty. He made her look like her writing. I gave him his money and he pulled a piece of tracing paper from a bag and laid it over the drawing, rolling it up tightly. He paused and quickly unrolled it, looking at his work one more time, as if he didn't want to let it go. Then, he took a pencil and signed the drawing in the corner, and again tied the rolled up work with a piece of thread and handed it back to me.

"Better save that," he said, "it'll be worth money someday.

I thanked him, and Elsie got one in on me as we walked away. "All you Americans, all you think about is your money!"

We laughed, but after that said nothing, which of course, begat a happy pause.

I spent another week in and around Copenhagen with Elsie before heading back to the states. We had talked of keeping the relationship going, but I don't know if either one of us really believed in the crux of our tale. There was an ocean and more between us, as the cliché goes, and at the airport, our conversation was filled with pauses that were neither happy nor sad, simply awkward. I don't believe in regret, but it's safe to say there are a few things I would've done differently in my yout. I don't think I was aware of the power of commitment — to a woman, a way of life, a principle — so I avoided them. Baseball was a strange kind of constant, the only thing that connected me to my youth and a time before I was called to make those sorts of decisions.

Over the years, I've gone to hundreds of baseball games, the majority in Wrigley Field, but also on little trips to major and minor league parks scattered across the country and beyond, in places like Mexico, the Dominican Republic, and Canada. I particularly enjoyed Montreal, for it reminded me of Copenhagen. I hadn't been back to Europe since Elsie and I drifted, so when I went up there, I spent some time before the game hanging around the old city, wandering, imagining how life might or might not have been different. My daydreams were so vivid, for a moment they became interchanged with real memories and I felt a wash of happiness, as if I was floating away on the waves that were just beyond my reach. Along the dock, I threw a coin into the water and made a wish, and despite my wish, the Giants beat the Cubs that night at Olympic Stadium, 5-3, and sadly, the Expos left Montreal.

Just the other day I was thinking of how I've sat in all parts of the field, from the first row behind the on-deck circle to the bleachers to the grandstand to the upper deck. And as much as I like to sit in the bleachers, I've never caught a foul ball or home run or batting practice fungo. I've never even had one come close. I think that would be a good litmus test for life's luck factor — sometimes people wind up with bruised fingers or sore palms, but a prize ball for their fate; others remain unscathed, but also empty-handed. The only thing left of Elsie, for me, is a framed charcoal drawing hanging in my baseball room. It's in the baseball room because Curt Flood signed it, the year he was painting for his principles in Copenhagen. It's strange to me how it flew over my head at the time, like a line drive I could never quite reach, how I didn't know the difference or could see how some people leave themselves out there in a strange place and wind up the better for it, making the impossible possible. Curt could read the crack of the bat well before anyone else, and so could Elsie, in her own way. I guess I'm still running through the grass, trying to catch up.

The Decathlon

jessica hollander

The first step is to lay out the course, pick the events, and choose the order. The next is to figure out a way to prevent Daniel from coming red-faced onto the porch halfway through the first race, crying, They're cheating! It's not fair! You're not yet sure if the second can be done.

Rummage through your drawer, full of medals from years of running, and pull out the one you're looking for: shiny gold with a picture of a man running and a great tree in the background. It has a thick ribbon attached at the top—red, white, and blue—which you intend to drape around the neck of the neighborhood champion.

It is your best one and for years it has remained weighed down by lesser medals. Attempt to smooth the kinks out of the ribbon. But they are 15-year-old wrinkles, determined to be remembered. Wrap the ribbon tightly around the cold, flat part of the medal and tuck it in your pocket.

At the kitchen table, tape four sheets of computer paper together and begin to plan the course. Draw a box for the house in the center; mark down the narrow driveway and the street it leads to so you know your limitations. Put in a few trees if you like, and if your backyard has a garden or a hill or sandbox, or a knee-high planter that's in the shape of a serpent, be sure to draw those too. They could serve as useful obstacles later on.

When your wife Cindy asks if you're going to waste the whole morning planning the decathlon, tell her yes. If she asks if you will be helping her clean or shop or mow the lawn, tell her no.

The race should start and end in the same place: next to the back porch. A red ribbon should be run from the house to the nearest tree for the winner to break through, hands held high, when the race is done. Gatorade must be ready to go around, preferably from a cooler, which can also be used to pour over the planner of the race, if the kids are so inclined.

After drawing a line with an arrow pointing to it and the words "red ribbon" written above, you may begin to plan the first event. The wheelbarrow race would be a good choice, as the paired nature of the event insures Daniel will not be the sole loser, and will then probably make it to the second event.

Draw a wheelbarrow next to the house and several dotted lines to the two large trees in the middle of your backyard. Do not worry if the wheels on your drawing are misshapen ovals and the handlebars much too long.

For the second event, perhaps the egg race. Quick, ask your wife before she goes to the store to pick up an extra dozen eggs. When she looks at you skeptically, assure her the point of the race is to *not* break the eggs. If you break the eggs, you lose. When she says, Man, you're really going to town with this aren't you, tell her: Yes. This is serious stuff. Hold up the medal with the red, white, and blue ribbon for her to see. Think fast if you need anything else from the store. (Perhaps a cooler for Gatorade?)

Didn't you win this at the Boston regional in college?

she's sure to ask. She will clutch at the medal and try to take it away from you. Her eyes will crinkle and grow small, her chin will barely support her frown.

Pull the medal away and hold it to your heart. Tell her you have a whole drawer full of medals, and besides, you are confident that Daniel will win and therefore keep the medal in the family. She will most likely shake her head at you then and give you a look you've seen her give dead birds on the sidewalk, not the bloody kind, but the still kind, the ones you almost think will hop to their feet and fly away before you notice the thick weightiness about them.

Return to the table and continue the plan. You will notice Daniel across from you, lining up ten small army men, his blond head and brown eyes half hidden by the stick bodies.

Tell him to go next door and then down the street, to inform the Campbells and the Rasheeds that the decathlon will start at 2:00. He will come around the table to look at you. Take the medal out of your pocket and show it to him. Watch his eyes grow big and mouth pop open. Tell him this is the grand prize.

Know he will go and describe the grand prize in exuberant detail, with fluttery hands and stuttering in his way.

When he is gone, look across at the green plastic men, with their guns and binoculars and flat little hats. The army men are hopeful. Go ahead and smile. Realize your son has some fight in him yet.

The third event will be the long jump into the sandbox. Then the hopping on one foot race, somersault race, obstacle course, egg hunt, tennis ball throw, and tire swing push.

The last event will be a race around the block, a course totaling three-quarters of a mile, taking them up and down steep hills and around sharp bends, on an unyielding sidewalk terrain.

The scoring will be this: for each event, ten points to the kid who wins, nine to the one in second, eight to the one in third, and so on, depending on the number of kids. When it is time for the final race event, add up all the points for each kid. Convert the points to seconds. The one winning so far will be given a head start of however many seconds he is ahead of the second place kid. The second place kid will be given a head start of however many seconds he is ahead of the third place kid, and so on. The winner of the final race will be the ultimate neighborhood champion and be given the illustrious medal in an elaborate award ceremony, held, of course, in the backyard.

Notice Daniel's ruddy face when he returns from spreading the news. He is excited, but you worry he is also on his way to being bright red and crying. Show him the map you've created; run your finger along the course and explain each event carefully. He will not say much in return, but you will tell by the way he leans toward the map and doesn't look away that he is paying close attention.

Take the medal out and let him hold it awhile; watch him turn it around in his hands. You know it won't be long before one of the neighborhood kids snatches it away. But it is a medal that must be won.

When the kids are lined up and you are ready to start, survey the participants with your arms crossed ceremoniously across your chest. There are a few you don't recognize. Word of the medal must have spread beyond the boundaries of the block.

A few of the kids shake their arms and neck, loosening up, and a few others gaze at you respectfully. There is one from next door, a small, quick kid named Noah, staring stoically past you. He has his hands on his waist, his elbows jutting out: the pose of a fighter. In a way, you respect this confidence. In a way, you hope he loses his footing in one of the early races and trips onto his face (it wouldn't hurt; the early races take place on the grass).

Then there is Daniel, the smallest of all, staring at you expectantly and clenching his fists.

When you believe the group to be at the height of tension, withdraw the medal from your pocket and thrust it into the air so it dangles from your hand and sparkles in the sun.

There will be gasps and squeals of excitement. Be prepared.

Announce the first event will be the wheelbarrow race and proceed to place them with partners. Put Noah and Daniel together; after all they are closest in size, and explain the point system as they position themselves into wheelbarrows and pushers. Know they will probably hear nothing you say.

Wave to your wife by the Egg Race and smile when she smiles at you. Notice the way she holds the stopwatch in one hand and angles the other hand down from her forehead to block out the sun, just as she used to do at your own races.

Pull out your whistle. Raise your hand above your head. On the count of three, drop your hand and blow the whistle. Watch them go. Watch Daniel push and Noah claw at the grass with his hands, pulling them both forward, into the lead. Grab your clipboard from the porch and run to your wife. Carefully record the order the contestants finish in and dole out the points. Daniel will jump up and down and you'll want to tell him to conserve his energy, but stop yourself. He will learn by himself, you think, if you let him.

For the next race, pass out the spoons. Carefully place an egg on the end of each and hope your excitable son does not drop his on the ground before the race even starts.

But he is surprisingly careful when the race begins. He leans his head toward the egg and pins his gaze on it like it will disappear into thin air if he looks away. He veers off course and heads for the tire swing. Run after him. Steer him back in the right direction. Watch him finish, the egg still in tact, fifteen seconds behind the rest.

Two kids have lost their eggs. Decide they will lose two points each for that. Pretend to ignore Noah kicking at the ground with his loose-sole sneaker.

After the long jump, hopping on one foot race, somersault race, obstacle course, egg hunt, tennis ball throw, and tire swing push, gather the breathy kids for the final event. There will be pain in their faces, but you are proud to see Daniel among them, bouncing on his heels. He will start the final race a full forty seconds behind Noah, the current winner, but he will be racing all the same.

Blow the whistle and watch Noah go, sprinting much too fast across the sidewalk. The other kids shuffle nervously beside you, but you know he'll never make it going that fast. Cindy signals that the next kid is up and you prepare him to go. Blow the whistle. Look at Daniel; he is scratching his leg with the heel of his shoe and rubbing both of his arms vigorously above the elbows, as though freezing.

Watch him shoot off like a pinball when it's his turn to go. Watch him round the corner and ignore the hook in your stomach that tries to pull you after him. Put your arms around your wife and feel her sigh into your chest.

You think he'll win? she'll ask. Tell her of course you do. You've known it all along.

Stay like that, believing what you said, until Noah comes sluggishly down the street and turns into the backyard. Run ahead of him with your hand in your wife's to witness him break the red ribbon and fall onto the grass with his tongue hanging out, with chokes and coughing sounds coming from his mouth. Run to the Gatorade and pour him a cup. Clap your hands as the rest of the kids finish. Clap your hands for when at last Daniel finishes, with sweat dripping down his cheeks, his face as red and puffy as a circus balloon.

Notice how he doesn't look at you. How he walks to between the big trees and collapses on the grass, just like the rest of the boys, but several yards away. Gather everyone around for the ceremony and shake your head at your wife when she makes a move to go see about Daniel. Let him sit out there by himself. From this distance, there are no such things as tears.

The Augustus Mackinnon Story

j. ryan stradal

"The motion of solid objects through space is one of the profound achievements of man," Augustus Mackinnon wrote his psychiatrist in 1976, while incarcerated in solitary confinement. "The idea that we can not only move ourselves and our own corporeal forms, but objects much heavier than ourselves — indeed, all of our possessions — from one point on a map to another, is literally astounding. However, attempting to replace them exactly as they were in a non-identical locale is as foolish as trying to re-write "The Wasteland" using bowling pins and mousetraps. A poem works because it is the perfect arrangement of words on a piece of paper, and a room works because it is the perfect arrangement of furniture within a three-dimensional space."

Like many great poets, Mackinnon found his voice while at odds with circumstance. The man *Paris Match* called "the Walt Whitman of furniture movers" graduated in 1956 from the now-defunct University of California, Calico, with an undergraduate degree in poetry, and moved to the coast to make his living as a poet. In need of sustenance and beguiled by an ad in the *Pasadena Instigator*, he was drawn to the discipline of furniture moving. Monotony and perambulation excited Mackinnon; he considered them "the Little and Big Dipper in the firmament of inspiration." He imagined a lifestyle where he would move furniture in the afternoon and write poetry at night.

There is no evidence, however, that Mackinnon ever wrote so much as a shopping list upon returning home at night. It is surmised that the physical rigors of his work left him exhausted, and the poems he wrote in his head on the job remained unwritten. "Poetry accumulated in his waking thoughts like letters in a dead man's mailbox," Edgar Caquill, Mackinnon's thesis advisor, conjectured. "Eventually, the box could hold no more."

Mackinnon felt that he just needed more time at the end of the day and decided that he was going to do his part to hasten every job, regardless of what his less-motivated colleagues thought. One afternoon, either September 5 (Reynold) or September 7 (Da Gamba), working through his lunch break, Mackinnon took a hope chest from the truck, walked it into the house, and for the first time, walked through the living room and placed it in the bedroom. The *Just Get In The House* era of furniture moving was over.

He didn't stop there; Mackinnon moved a mattress, bed frame, dresser, vanity, and chair into the bedroom before his colleagues even noticed. By the time they asked him what he was up to, Mackinnon's first piece, *14 Westminster Ave.* (1956), was nearly completed. Like many early works, it overreached—the hope chest blocked the door and the bed stuck out of the window—yet there was a grace, harmony, and logic to its arrangement. While looking at this room, Mackinnon realized he was reading. The furniture was in Iambic pentameter.

Over the following weeks, he developed a lexicon of furniture arrangement, or more to the point, a way of interpreting furniture arrangement, based on the rules of poetic versification his idealistic mind then valued. Among them:

Iambic: Where there are two or more pieces of furniture in a room and your attention is naturally drawn to the smaller, then larger pieces. Mackinnon first achieved this with his work *1429 Locust St.* (1957) by arraying the end tables with lime-green velvet and covering the lampshades with photographs of nude women. He later achieved the same end, less imprudently, with *5510 N. Somerset, Apt #B* (1960) by making every small piece of furniture a light fixture (even if that wasn't its especially designed purpose) and abbreviating their placement in the room with large pieces (sofas, divans, credenzas, etc.) upholstered or finished in dark colors.

Trochaic: Where there are two or more pieces of furniture in a room and your attention is drawn first to the larger, then smaller pieces. Arguably harder to achieve, a Trochee lacks the natural gravity of the Iambic arrangement. "No matter how you arrange furniture," Mackinnon observed, "in a room fitted with electricity, your eyes are drawn toward the light sources." After reading an article in *National Geographic* about large planets (e.g. Jupiter) that generate their own heat, Mackinnon first experimented with placing powerful light sources (e.g. klieg lights) inside the cushions of sofas and lounge chairs, hoping they would emanate a moody, luxurious glow. Sadly, the result caused copious, and nearly fatal, discomfort. Reviled by the trade publications (*Moving Man Monthly* called this experiment a "lose-lose situation") in the golden age of synthetic upholstery, this innovation created rooms that some furniture movers and consumer safety advocates decried as "fire hazards" or even "death traps".

Using a place with track lighting, skylights, and bay windows, Mackinnon attempted a Trochee with *122106 Cty. Rd. 6* (1967) and later, more forcibly, using kinetic, "robotic" furniture at *480 92nd St.* (1970). Both rooms were discredited as "cheating" by his peers, however, and proper Trochaic arrangement was to elude the frustrated Mackinnon his entire life.

Anapestic and **Dactylic**: Modes of arranging furniture in rooms of three pieces, used occasionally in hallways, and sometimes in bedrooms. In Anapestic arrangement, typified by the anteroom of *45789 Beechwood Ave.* (1959) one's attention is drawn first to the hat rack, then the lamp, and then finally the hope chest. Richelier Beauperdu, a leading interior design critic and innovator of the "Tragicomic" school of furniture arrangement, hastened to point out the munificence of the room's wainscoting in helping disguise 45789 Beechwood's hope chest. Mackinnon's response became the *cri du guerre* of the furniture metastasis scene: "I did not build the furniture. I did not build the room. I just build the art."

Infant's bedroom of 121 Farm St. (1963) is Mackinnon's most famous example of Dactylic arrangement. In this work, one's attention is drawn immediately to the bassinet, not to the chest of drawers or the end table. Whether or not the mysterious, cooing creature who inhabits the space is present, every clinical trial and beta test on this arrangement drew precisely the same result, with everyone not only immediately drawn to the bassinet, but instinctively looking inside it.

Finally, Mackinnon attempted **Spondaic Theory** (so called because it cannot be scientifically proven) several times. His most notable attempt was in the Spartan reception area of Arm & Balloon Real Estate for *711 Ventura Blvd.* (1965) where two identically sized pieces of furniture (in this case, desks) are said to draw one's attention simultaneously. Throughout the 1960s, the furniture transference community fiercely debated if such a phenomenon was physiologically possible. One has two eyes, so can one literally see two pieces of furniture in the same instant? The flat-earth types said no.

Spondaic Theory is possible in an arrangement sometimes known as a Mitchellette (probably after Jacquelin de Mitchellette [1931 – c. 1964], an interior designer of the Alexandrine school), who successfully achieved this phenomenon by placing two identically sized pieces of furniture directly beside each other. Most serious furniture movers, of course, reject the Mitchellette, calling it a "mindfuck."

Only time will tell if future generations warm up to Spondaic Theory, or if it will go the way of **Pyrrhic Theory** (a mode of arrangement where there are two pieces of furniture in a room, and you don't see either of them.)

With this innovative methodology, Augustus Mackinnon naturally became to furniture movers in the 1960s what Bob Dylan was to folk musicians, and likewise became a magnet for incredible adoration and criticism. As *Moving Man Monthly*'s "Mover of the Year" from 1964 – 1969, Mackinnon rewrote the rules of the furniture metastasis discipline, raising the eyebrows and stoking the ire of his conservative forebears, who grew to truly despise this talented young poet. His greatest enemy, however — and the person who destroyed his career — was an interior designer ten years his junior.

Annabella Silva Da Luca (1946 – 1975), a brilliant young Ph.D. in Comparative Literature from the University of Pennsylvania, followed many of her peers into the world of interior design. From her vantage point as editor of the alternative interior design quarterly *Milieu* she openly criticized what she called "the vainglorious and self-important work of furniture movers". Ultimately, bold statements such as this proved to be the tipping point in the decade-long battle between furniture movers and interior designers.

In 1970, the same year that *Moving Man Monthly* became *Mover's Monthly*, Mackinnon began responding to Da Luca with a few choice salvos of his own. "The interior designer is but a meretricious little pit-boss in an ivory tower, ignorant of real work," he wrote. "Only by handling furniture, suffering beneath its burdens, and working with its subtleties and nuances every day, would you have any knowledge on how or where to place it! These people, they touch a chair with nothing but their ass, and they should tell me where it goes?"

An event in spring 1971 shook the furniture transference and arrangement communities out of their scholarly cupboards to shatter against the freshly waxed linoleum floor of reason. A decree so simple, so instantly accepted, and so devastating, it instantly discredited all of Augustus Mackinnon's work, and in a week, brought his entire career to a standstill. Articles in *Milieu* had been picked up by major metropolitan papers before, but never one like this; a severe, paradigm-shattering tome by Annabella Silva Da Luca, with the heart-breaking headline "Light Fixtures Are Not Furniture."

Light Fixtures Are Not Furniture. The phrase was out there, it was in the world, and people read it and believed it, whether they believed it or not. Mackinnon was shattered; he didn't move so much as a folding chair for eight months. All of his work, the Iambs, the Trochees, the Anapests, were all dependent on light fixtures as key components in the vocabulary of furniture.

Mackinnon did not take this widely accepted revelation well. "All things are furniture," he wrote in fall 1971. "Any object I can see, that I can touch, that I can move, that inhabits space within a room, is FURNITURE! My shoes, when I remove them, are furniture—a pencil on a desk is furniture, the dust on the fridge is furniture! All things are furniture, and furniture is all things."

Mackinnon's bombastic tirade won him a little sympathy but no converts. "He took things too far," claimed lyric poet and furniture mover Viola Da Gamba (1946–1987). "I certainly didn't want to go over to his house and just be 'furniture' to him. What's more, he was getting intolerable to be with in public—every restaurant we'd go to, he'd point at a lamp and ask the waiter 'Is that furniture?' And if they didn't give him an answer he liked, he'd storm out. So embarrassing. And worse, he made these little stickers that said FURNITURE and stuck them all over the city. Everywhere, on light posts, mailboxes, moving vehicles. Once, well, I got a little tipsy and ended up staying overnight at his place, and I woke up the next morning to find him putting those FURNITURE stickers all over my clothes. That was it. I just couldn't take it anymore. It's sad, very sad, really, what happened to him."

In October 1972, Augustus Mackinnon was blacklisted from the pages of *Mover's Monthly* by popular demand. He went into hiding and disappeared from the face of the earth, not even communicating with his family. It was almost two years later when Mackinnon returned to the public eye; on August 5th, 1975, in a New York City walkup, he attended a crime scene, where the body of Annabella Silva Da Luca had been rent asunder with a fire axe and scattered about a small room.

One couldn't help but notice upon entering the apartment that one's attention was immediately diverted to the severed head, and then to the smaller, mutilated extremities, making *117 Perry St.* (1975) an undisputed example of proper Trochaic arrangement.

My Totally Awesome Funeral

curtis smith

No viewing parlors with their embedded stink of old women's perfume and phony propriety. Throw a bash at my crib instead—ain't nothing like a house party—the price of admission a single wood scrap salvaged from the cobwebbed corners of basements and garages. Arrange a heap by the door and let the handiest and most ambitious guests hammer these misfits into my farewell vessel. Buy me a suit coat at the flea market, a sherbet-colored eyesore at least three sizes too big, and fill my pockets with verses of poetry and the old photographs that never made it into the family album, the shut-eyed portraits, the embarrassing shots of pale skin and tummy rolls taken from our beach vacations. Tell the undertaker to work a smartass grin onto my face. Paint *Hello!* on one closed eyelid, *Goodbye!* on the other. Entertain my son with a magic trick, and if he laughs, do it again. Ask my wife if she's lost weight. Buy the expensive beer and wine I never thought I deserved in life and make sure no glass goes empty. Play music all night long—Jelly

Roll, Louis and the Hot Fives, and once the vibe grows ragged and sloppy, crank out "Iron Man" until the speakers crackle and the stomp of beat-keeping shoes sends every shelved knickknack tumbling to the floor. Carry me to the backyard and lay me on a picnic table beneath the stars—I've always preferred the company of outcasts and smokers. Drink to absent friends. Drink another just because you can. After my wife and son have gone to bed, let the hard-core partiers highjack me for one last ride—shotgun!—and no matter the season, roll down the window and let the wind lash my hair. Drive to the old quarry and drag me to the north face's steep cliff, the one I was always afraid to jump from into the cold, deep water below, and prop me against the cliff's crowning forty-foot hemlock while my friends yell and sing off-key into the darkness, a serenade echoed back from the circling vista of stone.

Hold the service at sundown the next day at the old drive-in, the one with the waist-high weeds straining between the macadam cracks, where the rusting speaker poles cast stretching, sundial shadows over a moonscape of broken glass and wind-swept trash. Monkeys, there must be monkeys, monkeys in red fezzes and roller skates, burning sparklers grasped in their paws. And while you're at the zoo, procure a giraffe or two to lope around the perimeter, their curious heads poking through the screen's tattered panels. Give the children noisemakers and encourage them to blow and toot until they're forced to lay their swooning heads in their mothers' laps. Hire a marginally talented mime to wander among the mourners—his glass wall routine both symbolic that we spend our lives trapped in little boxes and also a reminder that we should be eternally thankful that most of our boxes don't have mimes. Let my son wear his Superman cape if he wants. Break into the projection booth, switch on the static-spitting speakers, and broadcast a tape of a newborn's first cry. The recording can be of any baby, it doesn't matter. Tell my wife she looks great in black. Construct my eulogy with dialogue snippets culled from old Brat Pack movies and deliver them with a straight face. Relay this single message from me: "I had fun. Really." Adorn my old girlfriends in pink widow's veils and Victoria's Secret smuttery, and have them sing an a cappella version of "Just a Gigolo."

As the light fades from the sky, stuff my casket with the drafts of my stories that went nowhere, the novels that sagged beneath the weight of their own pretensions. Let the giraffes wander the lot's edges, their shambling grace on display as they nibble the offerings of the surrounding trees. Allow my wife and me a private moment, a final goodbye before nailing the coffin shut with one last ill-fitting piece and dousing the wood with lighter fluid. Commission a dozen archers to shoot flaming arrows—high, arcing trajectories that trace the bruised sky like so many shooting stars. Hug the person next to you as the arrows thud into the wood. Stay for a bit to study the knotted smoke plumes, the orange sparks that leap higher than the rest, but leave, with monkeys and giraffes in tow, before the flames die.

After I'm gone, visit the monkeys and giraffes at the zoo. Part of me, I believe, will be waiting in their dark eyes. Unspeaking, unjudging, I will gaze upon you with all the wonder and amazement you deserve.

Dragster 2 (Dragster Series), 1995
Perry Vasquez
Recycled Havoline 10w-30
on Arches print paper
22" x 30"

Contributors
(in alphabetical order)

David Barringer is the author of the novel, *Johnny Red*, and the book of autobiographical design criticism, *American Mutt Barks in the Yard*. He has recently written for *I.D. Magazine*, *Eye Magazine*, *Emigre*, *Voice*, and *SpeakUp*. He designs books for Word Riot Press, Opium Magazine, and Triple Press. His interview with George Saunders will appear in the summer 2006 issue of *Barrelhouse*. Contact: www.davidbarringer.com.

Dennis Dillingham earned a Bachelor of Arts degree in English with honors from the College of the Holy Cross in Worcester, Massachusetts. His publishing history includes the short story "The White Carousel Horse," which was selected as a finalist for the MTV–Pocket Books Short Story Contest for Young Writers. The story subsequently appeared in the book *Pieces–A Collection of New Voices*, edited by Stephen Chbosky (author of *Perks of Being a Wallflower*) and published by Pocket Books in August 2000. Since then his work has appeared in various print and web journals. Dennis currently works as a research manager for Weber Shandwick Worldwide in Chicago, where he lives with his wife Vanessa and pug Penelope, both adopted Mets' fans.

George Ducker grew up in Greenville, South Carolina and has lived in various parts of Illinois and California. His work has appeared or is forthcoming in *Los Angeles Magazine* and the *Santa Monica Review.*

Anne Elliott has performed her poetry, with and without ukulele, at Lincoln Center, PS122, Exit Art, and the Whitney Museum. Her fiction has appeared most recently in *Pindeldyboz* (web), and she blogs on the writing life and feral cat management at http://www.assbackwords.blogspot.com. She lives in Brooklyn.

Lauren Groff was born and raised in Cooperstown, N.Y., and has just completed her MFA in fiction at the University of Wisconsin-Madison. Her recent work is forthcoming in *Washington Square, Beloit Fiction Journal,* and the *Atlantic Monthly.* She will be the 2006-2008 Axton Fellow in Fiction at the University of Louisville, where she plans to finish a novel and collection of stories.

Raised in Chicago and residing in Nashville, singer-songwriter **Doug Hoekstra**'s perchance for painting musical landscapes has been lauded by critics, djs, and fans throughout the United States and Europe, earning him a reputation as a man with an ear for a phrase and an eye for detail. In addition to touring extensively and releasing seven CDs on labels on both sides of the pond, Hoekstra has also written and placed short fiction and non-fiction in numerous literary journals. His first-full-length collection, *Bothering the Coffeedrinkers,* appeared in 2006 and one of the tales from that work, "The Blarney Stone," has been nominated for a Pushcart Prize. For more on Doug's many moods, go to:
www.doughoekstra.com or www.myspace.com/doughoekstra

Jessica Hollander grew up and went to school in Ann Arbor, Michigan, her favorite place on earth except for during the winters. She now lives in North Carolina and recently received a United Arts grant from the state for writing. Her stories have appeared or are forthcoming in *Denver Syntax, Electric Current, Wandering Army, Spotlight,* and the *Scruffy Dog Review.*

Nick Johnson is an English teacher living in Santa Monica, California with his wife and two children. His stories have appeared in *Threepenny Review* and *Confrontation.* Occasionally he writes (and even edits) films for the illustrious and ever-so-slightly unhinged Christopher Coppola. He recently completed work on his first novel.

Douglas Light is the author of the novel *East Fifth Bliss* (Behler). His writing has appeared or is forthcoming in the *New York Times*, the *Alaska Quarterly Review*, *KGB Bar LIT*, *Pindeldyboz*, *Night Train*, and *Failbetter*, and in the anthologies *O. Henry Prize Stories* and the *Best American Nonrequired Reading.*

Ginny MacKenzie's manuscript, *Skipstone*, won the 2002 Backwaters Press Poetry Competition. Her short stories, poems, and creative nonfiction have appeared in many anthologies and magazines, including *New Letters*, *Ploughshares*, *Agni Review*, *Boulevard*, *Crab Orchard Review*, *The Nation*, *Pequod*, *The Threepenny Review*, *Poetry East*, *American Literary Review*, and *Prairie Schooner.* She lives in New York City and is working on a novel and a new book of poetry.

Christopher Orlet was born in a log cabin in Southern Illinois. Unnecessarily. His stories have appeared in *The Simpering Nautilus*, *Inside the Female Ear*, *The Happy Hyena*, *High Noon at Midnight*, and many other high-brow publications.

J. Chris Rock lives in one of the many Springfields sprinkled across the United States. His writing has recently appeared in *Barrelhouse*, *The Science Creative Quarterly*, and *McSweeney's Internet Tendency.*

Curtis Smith's stories and essays have appeared in dozens of literary journals including *American Literary Review*, *Mid-American Review*, *CutBank*, *Passages North*, *Greensboro Review*, *Night Train*, *Mississippi Review*, and many others. March Street Press has released two collections of his short-short stories. His first novel, *An Unadorned Life*, was released in 2003; his next, *Between Sound and Noise*, will be out later this year.

J. Ryan Stradal grew up in Minnesota. He now lives in Venice, CA and recently completed his first novel. This story is dedicated to his late mother, who earned her English degree when he was a little boy and used her reading assignments as bedtime stories.

Perry Vasquez is an artist living in San Diego, California. Throughout the 90s and 00s, Perry worked on developing an array of unique artistic practices including Motography which is the use of recycled motor oil for fine art monoprinting. He also developed a number of interactive artworks using tape loops, motion detectors and sound collages. He has a wife named Rondi and a 19 month-old son named Trey.

Shellie Zacharia's fiction has appeared in *Swivel, Washington Square, Dos Passos Review, Small Spiral Notebook, Vestal Review*, and other journals. She teaches in Gainesville, Florida.

Catherine Zeidler has an MFA from the University of Michigan and works in finance for the United Nations Office of Project Services. "Pregnant" is her first published story; she would like to thank you in advance for all the beautiful flowers.